Erika Harvey was editor of *Here's Health* and *Parents* and now works as a freelance writer for various other health, childcare and general interest magazines. She is a member of the Guild of Health Writers.

THE ELEMENT GUIDE SERIES

The *Element Guide* series addresses important
psychological and emotional issues in a clear,
authoritative and straightforward manner. The
series is designed for all people who deal with these
issues as everyday challenges. Each book explores
the background, possible causes and symptoms
where appropriate, and presents a comprehensive
approach to coping with the situation. Each book
also includes advice on self-help, as well as where –
and when – to turn for qualified help. The books are
objective and accessible, and lead the reader to a
point where they can make informed decisions
about where to go next.

Titles in the Element Guide series

Addictions by Deirdre Boyd
Anorexia & Bulimia by Julia Buckroyd
Anxiety, Phobias & Panic Attacks by Elaine Sheehan
Bereavement by Ursula Markham
Childhood Trauma by Ursula Markham
Depression by Sue Breton
Insomnia by Dr Dilys Davies
Low Self-Esteem by Elaine Sheehan
Miscarriage by Ursula Markham
Postnatal Depression by Erika Harvey
Shyness by Rochelle Simmons
Stress by Lynne Crawford and Linda Taylor

POSTNATAL DEPRESSION

Your Questions Answered

Erika Harvey

ELEMENT

Shaftesbury, Dorset • Boston, Massachusetts
Melbourne, Victoria

© Element Books Limited 1999
Text © Erika Harvey 1999

First published in the UK in 1999 by
Element Books Limited
Shaftesbury, Dorset SP7 8BP

Published in the USA in 1999 by
Element Books, Inc.
160 North Washington Street
Boston, MA 02114

Published in Australia in 1999 by
Element Books and distributed by
Penguin Australia Limited
487 Maroondah Highway, Ringwood, Victoria 3134

Erika Harvey has asserted her right under the Copyright, Designs and Patents
Act, 1988 to be identified as the author of this work.

Cover design by The Bridgewater Book Company
Design by Roger Lightfoot
Typeset by WestKey Limited, Falmouth, Cornwall
Printed and bound in Great Britain by
Biddles Ltd, Guildford & King's Lynn

British Library Cataloguing in Publication
data available

Library of Congress Cataloging in Publication data

Harvey, Erika.
    The postnatal depression : your questions answered / Erika Harvey.
        p.   cm. — (The Element guide)
    Includes bibliographical references and index.
    ISBN 1–86204–330–2 (pbk. : alk. paper)
    1. Postpartum depression—Popular works.   I. Title.   II. Series:
Element guide series.
RG852.H37   1999
618.7′6—dc21   98–46429
                                                                                      CIP

ISBN 1 86204 330 2

Note from the Publisher

Any information given in any book in the *Element Guide* series is not intended
to be taken as a replacement for medical advice. Any person with a condition
requiring medical attention should consult a qualified medical practitioner or
suitable therapist.

Contents

Introduction

Before you actually hold your baby in your arms, it is hard to imagine what life will be like as a mother. You think about the practical side – the feeding, the bathing, the nappies – and the lovingness – the holding, the cuddling and the comforting. What you do not think about is that this baby may plunge you into a deep well of blackest despair – perhaps making you so depressed that you may feel you do not love your baby, that you do not want to be with him and that you do not like being a mother.

This was certainly not something I expected to experience. When I became pregnant with my first child, Joseph, I was editor of a parenting magazine. I knew all the theory, all the background, all the reasons why it was better to do one thing rather than another. I had read all that the baby books had to say on the early days with a newborn. I felt I went into parenthood fully prepared and with my eyes wide open.

But things did not match my plans. Joseph's birth was long and difficult, culminating in a Ventouse delivery and a lot of stitches. I was determined to breastfeed, but somehow Joe and I just could not get it right; it became excruciatingly painful and so I stopped breastfeeding after 10 days and turned, guiltily, to formula milk.

Joseph was not a difficult baby, but he cried a lot and inconsolably. It seemed that nothing I did was right. I felt alone and lonely, longing for adult company. I had never spent very much time at home, having always worked full-time, and had no friends nearby who were also at home with children. My husband was away at work, as were my other close relatives. I hardly went out, which made days with the baby long and gruelling, and as he became bored I became irritated, frustrated, and depressed.

Depression for me was a slow slide into greyness, carrying a heaviness that ate up my energy and enthusiasm for life. Everything was a supreme effort – even playing with the baby. By two months Joe had settled into a reasonable sleep routine, but I was still tired all the time and could not sleep. I was tetchy and irritable towards my husband and in a constant state of semi-anger with the baby, blaming him (unreasonably, of course) for putting me into a position where I could not cope.

Sadly, it was only on my return to work when Joe was four months old that I managed to rise above the depression. Suddenly, I had renewed energy and interest in life, and could actually start enjoying my baby.

I never sought professional help for my depression, feeling it was not serious enough – and in this I was like a lot of depressed mothers, many of whom in fact have depression much more severely than I did. Official figures put the incidence of postnatal depression at between 10 and 20 per cent of new mothers, but many primary care health workers put the figure much higher – at nearer 60 per cent of postnatal mothers suffering a degree of depression worse than the 'baby blues'. The discrepancy between these figures highlights the number of depressed new mothers who do not come forward for help and who slip through the healthcare net – either because there is insufficient postnatal screening for depression or because the mother herself takes pains to hide her true feelings from her family doctor or health professionals at the child clinic.

So, if you are suffering from postnatal depression, you are certainly not alone. But why should postnatal depression be a continuing problem, now that women are, for the most part, far more in control of their lives than previous generations? We are able to plan when to have a baby, and enjoy our independence until we're ready to start a family; our partners are now much more likely to be involved with the baby, and *support* the mother in her mothering; we have endless gadgets in the home to make domestic life easier; and, for many women, there is an option to return to work after the baby is born, with companies becoming much more flexible with regard to maternity leave, part-time work and working hours.

But sadly, it seems that although modern life *is* in many respects 'better' for women than ever before, the *way* we live has made it harder for women to make the adjustment to motherhood – and health experts have actually started to see as significant a new mother's domestic and social situation and even psychological make-up when attempting to pinpoint those who may be susceptible to postnatal depression. No longer is postnatal depression viewed simply as a problem to do with hormones which will settle down in time; postnatal depression is now being taken seriously.

Although often postnatal depression is lumped in with other common features of new parenthood, such as sleepless nights, a crying baby and difficulties with breastfeeding, it is painfully clear is that it is not a problem which should be ignored: postnatal depression touches so many vulnerable people – mother, baby, father, and other children in the family. It is a significant problem and can be terrifying to a new mother, in part because it is something which comes from inside us yet is beyond our control, and our emotions and thoughts. In postnatal depression it can seem as though you have lost that control.

Medium to severe postnatal depression can also last much longer than crying or breastfeeding troubles. Colicky screaming abates in most babies by around four months, and breastfeeding is usually in a routine by two weeks after the birth. If postnatal depression goes untreated, however, it can take months to get over and many women feel they never get back to being their old selves. It can also have a devastating effect on the whole family, putting both parents under immense strain, interfering with the normal development of the mother/baby relationship and – if it is depression with a second or subsequent birth – having a knock-on effect on any other children in the family.

But there is much that can be done to treat postnatal depression: treatments which we know work well, whether you need drug therapy or are offered a 'talking' approach such as counselling or psychotherapy. Complementary and alternative approaches are also showing that they are very effective when it comes to depression – including postnatal depression – so this extends the choice of treatments on offer, whether you opt to try a completely alternative approach or combine conventional medical treatment with complementary therapies.

In addition, as I hope to show, there is a lot you can do for yourself – even if that self-help is simply admitting you are depressed and seeing a doctor. You have already made your first step in helping yourself climb out of depression – you are reading this book . . .

Note: To avoid clumsy constructions, I have used 'he' and 'she' in alternate chapters when the sex of the baby or person is indeterminate but either stands for both genders. In addition, because healthcare systems in different countries vary greatly, I have used the term 'health professional' to cover every trained healthcarer involved in a woman's postnatal care.

CHAPTER 1

What is Postnatal Depression?

The medical profession tends to list postnatal depression as a subcategory of general depression because it shares many of the symptoms. General depression is often triggered by a traumatic life event or change, for example, losing your job, going through a divorce, or after losing a loved one. Postnatal depression can follow childbirth. Having a baby – particularly your first baby – is one of the greatest life changes we can experience – altering a woman's life, expectations and view of herself dramatically. Because of this, it is obviously an experience which carries with it a high risk of depression.

But postnatal depression is different from general depression in a number of ways. It is:

- associated with a specific trigger – that is, the change in roles, relationships and personal circumstances after having a baby;
- possibly caused by the hormonal upheavals which occur around the time of the birth and in the weeks following;
- usually confined to a particular time – the first six months to a year after childbirth.

Doctors divide the phenomenon of postnatal mood changes into three categories: the 'blues', postnatal depression itself (which varies from mild to severe) and puerperal psychosis.

THE BABY BLUES

'Just after the birth, I was so happy I was high. Then, on around the second day when my milk started to come in, I just went down like a balloon. I felt so sad. Anything would start me crying for no reason at all.' Sharon, mother of six-week-old Bethany.

It is estimated that up to 85 per cent of new mothers experience postpartum 'blues', also often called the two- (or three-or ten-) day blues because it occurs in the first two weeks after the birth. The blues are almost certainly caused by the hormonal changes which occur in the body directly after the birth, when high levels of hormones like oestrogen and progesterone suddenly plummet. The symptoms include feeling 'down', tiredness, difficulty sleeping, sudden worries and anxieties, lack of concentration, lack of appetite, oversensitivity and snappiness; but its main symptom is a general, all-enveloping weepiness. New mothers with the baby blues will cry at the least thing; one mum remembers breaking down while watching a nappy advertisement on TV.

The baby blues are not serious, last only a few days and are gone two weeks after the birth. No medical help is required at this point; all that is really needed is a supportive, non-judgmental shoulder to cry on. Talking to the family doctor or another health professional may help, as he will be able to offer reassurance that your feelings are normal, and also offer you support if there are any other problems which may be making the blues worse, such as a crying baby, breastfeeding difficulties or any family problems or worries. There are many organizations which offer support for particular problems, and you may prefer to contact them directly. La Leche League, for example, offers support and practical advice to those wishing to breastfeed and has trained breastfeeding counsellors who can help you to get feeding up and running well. (See Useful Addresses, p. 116)

PUERPERAL PSYCHOSIS

'Sonia changed into someone else after William was born. She bounced between being hyperactive, over-talkative and obsessed with William's wellbeing, to distant, lethargic and depressed. She was obsessed with germs and would clean William's stuff – his cot, his toys and so on – over and over. She seemed convinced that she wasn't looking after him properly and that someone would come and take him away. Then she started talking about people coming to the house while I was at work, trying to take him from her. I called the health centre and talked to our doctor. She was very sympathetic but also worried when I told her what was going on. Finally speaking to someone who understood was such a relief, I just broke down. The next day, Sonia was taken into hospital, where she stayed for several weeks. She was on antidepressants backed up by counselling for around eight months after that.' Douglas, father of two-year-old William.

This is postpartum or puerperal psychosis. It is at the other end of the scale to the 'blues', being the most serious – but thankfully rare – form of postnatal depressive illness. It affects up to two new mothers per thousand, and often these are women who have a history of depression or who have depressive illness in the family. Unfortunately, suffering from it in one pregnancy increases the likelihood of it developing in any subsequent pregnancies.

Like the 'blues', puerperal psychosis usually develops soon after the birth, often within the first two weeks and usually within the first month. Unlike the 'blues', however, the symptoms are severe: deep depression, mood swings (from depression to hyperactive mania), hearing voices, seeing things, and losing a grip on reality. A mother suffering from puerperal psychosis may become unhealthily obsessed with her baby and his wellbeing, may reject him completely, or may think about harming herself or the baby. In some rare cases, mothers have turned these thoughts into action and, for this reason, someone suffering from puerperal psychosis will be offered urgent treatment and may need to be hospitalized for both her own and the baby's safety.

On the positive side, most cases of puerperal psychosis respond to treatment, with most patients improving in around three months. The important step in cases of psychosis is to seek help immediately. Since the illness often develops in the first days after the birth, the symptoms are usually obvious enough to be picked up by health-care professionals still checking up on mother and baby in the immediate postnatal period. If, however, the symptoms develop later, it will be up to you or those close to you to seek help. Psychosis is a serious illness; the sooner treatment begins, the better for mother, baby and the family.

POSTNATAL DEPRESSION

'I felt like I'd entered some dark, nightmare world where everything jangled my nerves and every movement was an effort. I was going through the motions of doing things – feeding her, bathing her, holding her – but I didn't feel any connection. I didn't feel I loved her although I pretended I did and then I felt guilty about having to pretend. I really wanted to scream out, "Take her away. I want to sleep, I want to get out of the house, I want to be myself again".'
Felicity, mother of one-year-old Libby.

Postnatal depression itself can start soon after the birth or as long as six months to a year later. Although there is currently little research into the causes of postnatal depression, there appear to be several factors which make a new mother more susceptible to developing the condition, and this is covered in detail in the next chapter. The symptoms are quite wide-ranging (see Symptoms of Depression, p. 5), but the constant emotion is unremitting lowness of mood. In addition, there is a loss in the ability to be interested or excited in anything and life is a dreary shade of grey; coping with the baby is difficult and any set-back is enough to trigger despondency, frustration or lethargy. There may be

Symptoms of Depression
The following is an internationally accepted criteria for diagnosing a depressive disorder like postnatal depression:

Feeling depressed and being unable to take any interest or pleasure in anything. This symptom will be with you constantly, plus five or more of the following:

- weight loss or weight gain
- increase or decrease in appetite
- problems sleeping, or sleeping too much
- waking early in the morning and being unable to get back to sleep
- feeling agitated and restless to such a degree that other people notice
- tiredness and loss of energy
- inability to concentrate or make decisions
- feeling worthless and inappropriately guilty
- feeling that you are not a good mother or you are not taking care of the baby properly
- feeling things are getting on top of you
- thoughts of death and suicide, even to the point of planning suicide.

The more symptoms you have in addition to feeling generally low, then the more severe the depression is likely to be. With mild depression, you will be low in spirits generally but able to continue with your normal everyday life. In moderate depression, symptoms may be more obvious to other people and it is usually more difficult to get through everyday activities. With severe depression, life is badly affected: it is very difficult to function as normal, and symptoms are marked.

If you have experienced these symptoms for two weeks without let-up, then it is highly possible that you have postnatal depression and so should seek the advice of your doctor immediately. The doctor will need to double-check that the depression is not caused by some other problem, as well as getting you started quickly on a treatment programme.

seemingly irrational frustration or anger, and this may be directed at a partner. Often there is a withdrawal from social contact, preferring to stay in with the baby, and deliberate avoidance of other people.

Unfortunately, postnatal depression is often missed by healthcare professionals, even though they are in contact with the mother. This is partly because many mothers make an effort to hide their depression; they do not want anyone to know they cannot cope or are ashamed to admit they are depressed. Many people still believe that there is some stigma attached to having a mental health problem and so there is a natural reluctance for some of us to admit to feeling low or overwhelmed. Felicity admits:

> 'I knew I wasn't coping, I knew I was depressed, but I couldn't bring myself to tell anyone. I certainly didn't want it on my medical records that I'd flipped, that a baby had got the better of me. It wasn't until I was sitting on an empty bus one day and found myself thinking I'd leave Libby there – and actually getting up ready to do it – that I realized I had to get some help. Even then, I didn't approach my doctor. I spoke to my midwife and she put me in touch with a local postnatal support group. I can't tell you the relief I felt at that first meeting when I found I wasn't alone in feeling so down and despairing.'

Postnatal depression is sometimes also missed because some of the symptoms are natural features of the days following birth. Appetite and weight tend to fluctuate in the early days after delivery because you are grabbing a meal or snack when the baby allows. All new mothers suffer from broken nights, and so are tired and lethargic. In the early days, too, many mothers have problems concentrating or making decisions because, firstly, they are tired and, secondly, they are thinking about so many baby-related things that it is difficult to think past them. Finally, there are few new mothers who do not feel, at some point, that everything is getting on top of them.

The difference with postnatal depression is that these symptoms are experienced almost constantly; they will also be noticeable to other people, and they will be accompanied by distinct emotions, like feelings of inadequacy, guilt, anxiety, anger, and overwhelming lassitude or despondency.

When It Isn't Postnatal Depression

Depression can be a symptom of another illness, so it is always advisable to see your doctor, even if you believe you only feel mildly depressed. Other illnesses which may be mistaken for depression include the following:

Anaemia Iron deficiency is common during and after pregnancy, because the baby has taken the mother's iron stores from her while in the womb. Losing a lot of blood after the birth can also cause iron deficiency. One of the main symptoms of this form of anaemia is depression, along with fatigue, pallor, poor appetite, nausea, dizziness and palpitations. Treatment is with iron supplementation.

Post-pregnancy thyroid disorder (thyroiditis) Around six to seven per cent of women suffer some disturbance of the thyroid gland after giving birth. This is estimated to account for around 10 per cent of new mothers suffering from postnatal depression. With this condition, the thyroid either under- or over-produces the hormones thyroxine and triiodothyronine, producing a range of symptoms. An overactive thyroid (hyperthyroidism) can cause mood swings and anxiety; an underactive thyroid (hypothyroidism) causes lethargy, poor concentration and depression. Depending on the type of thyroid disorder, treatment will include either hormone replacement to raise thyroid hormone levels, or a blocker, which stops hormones being produced. The condition usually rights itself within six months following the birth.

Drug-induced depression This is a side-effect of many pharmaceutical preparations, so check if you have started taking a new drug which could be causing your depressed symptoms. *However, do not stop taking the drugs, without consulting your doctor*. Drugs which can cause depression include tranquillizers, sleeping pills, beta-blockers, drugs for high blood pressure, steroids, anticonvulsants, antibiotics, some nonsteroidal anti-inflammatories and the oral contraceptive pill.

Health professionals involved in the care of mother and baby are now becoming much more vigilant in checking for signs of postnatal depression. This means that check-ups may not focus solely on the baby and your physical wellbeing, but also include questions about your emotional state and how you are coping. You may be asked, for example, what kind of help are you getting at home? Do you have time for yourself? Do you have any concerns about your health? Have you ever had any problems with depression? You may even be asked to fill in a questionnaire featuring questions aimed at finding out just how you are feeling and how you are coping. This is so that fewer new mothers slip through the net. Now is the time to be honest and to admit if you are not coping, or if you have been suffering any of the symptoms outlined here. It is all right to admit all's not well.

If the health professionals caring for you do not pick up on your depression but you are aware that it may be a problem, then contact your doctor. Also, try to assess how you feel about yourself, your situation, your baby and your partner. What is your primary emotion (apart from depression) – guilt, frustration, or anger? How do these emotions show themselves? At whom are they directed? When is it worse for you? Does anything help? Be honest, too, about any relationship problems between you and your partner, and if these problems existed before the baby came along or if they are new, since the baby's arrival. Knowing these things will help your doctor assess how urgent your need for help is and to devise an appropriate treatment programme.

It is important that you seek help. Healthcare professionals are well aware of the existence of postnatal depression, of how common it is and the damage it can do. They will not judge you or think you a bad mother, they will only want to help. Suffering in silence, trying to cope when you feel out of control, stifling feelings, feeling guilty when those feelings erupt, struggling to get through the day, every day, is no way to begin family life.

Why See A Doctor?
If you have postnatal depression, it is easy to put off seeing a doctor, but there are compelling reasons why you should seek outside help.

- Feeling depressed after childbirth is common and curable but can cause damage. It is a condition which has knock-on effects for the family, so quick treatment can avoid wider complications. Trying to pull yourself through depression may take longer than it would if you sought treatment.
- It may be that there is something else causing your depression, like anaemia or thyroid problems. Your doctor will need to treat you for this.

Your doctor can offer support and advice as well as a sympathetic ear and he can recommend you to a trained counsellor if necessary.

CHAPTER 2

Why Me?

If you suffer from postnatal depression, it is easy to compare yourself with other mothers and ask why they don't feel the same way as you do. Why should they be lucky enough to escape the weight of depression, frustration and anger and not you? What makes them different?

The short answer is that everyone is different: everyone's life, history and personality is unique and it is these things which have a bearing on whether we become depressed or not. Let us take some examples.

Laura and Stephanie are in a similar situation when they have their first baby. Each has waited until their early thirties before starting a family. Both have a fulfilling career, enjoy their work and intend to return to work after maternity leave. Both have supportive husbands and there are no financial problems. In each case, the baby is a much-wanted and planned addition to the family. Laura develops postnatal depression; Stephanie does not.

Charlie and Tonya are single mothers, both aged 18. Each lives alone with her baby in rented accommodation; neither works and money is tight. Each has little to do with the father of the baby and each is happy to have minimal contact. There is no other boyfriend on the scene. Charlie breezes through the first year with her baby; Tonya becomes severely depressed.

The differences between these two sets of women lie in aspects of their personality and situation which may not be immediately apparent. Laura, for instance, is used to controlling her life. She is a department manager at a large financial institution and prides herself on running the department like clockwork. Stephanie is a textile designer with a small company, who enjoys a lot of freedom in how she works. Laura did not have the birth she wished for. She went over her due date by two weeks, labour was induced and finally the baby delivered by Caesarean. A few days later she developed an uterine infection. Between the Caesarean stitches and the infection, Laura found breast-feeding very uncomfortable and had difficulty getting the baby interested in feeding. She began to feel the situation was spiralling downward beyond her control, that she could do nothing right, and that her baby did not like her.

Stephanie, on the other hand, went into labour sponta-neously and had a straightforward delivery, apart from an episiotomy to help her 9 lb baby into the world. The baby took to breastfeeding immediately and Stephanie entered motherhood confident and relaxed.

Although Charlie has no partner she does have a supportive and loving family who live nearby. She has two other sisters, one who is married with children, and another who is usually available for babysitting. In addi-tion, Charlie's mother does not work so is available to her daughter on a regular basis, and has already told Charlie that she will look after the baby should Charlie wish to get a job.

Tonya grew up in care and has no contact with her family. Her own mother had mental health problems and Tonya was taken into care at age six for her own safety. Having moved around a lot since she was 16, she does not have any close friends, so there is no-one to whom she can turn for support, beyond the social workers who call regularly but of whom Tonya is suspicious. There is little prospect of Tonya getting a job and she is finding it increasingly hard to survive on welfare benefits. Her baby is the focus of her life, but she feels she is a poor mother: as Tonya puts it, 'I love him but I feel sorry for him, having me as his mum. I wish he could have done better.'

What these women show is that there are many variables involved in who gets postnatal depression. These variables break down into three categories: biological factors, social factors and personality/psychological make-up.

BIOLOGICAL FACTORS

With postnatal depression, there are two biological ways of approaching what is happening in the body and how this may trigger the problem.

First, there is the role of chemicals in the brain responsible for regulating mood. These chemicals are called neurotransmitters because they transmit messages about our thoughts, feelings, impulses and decisions – as well as when to sleep, eat and so on – from one nerve cell (neurone) to another. The main neurotransmitters thought to be involved in depression are serotonin, noradrenaline (norepinephrine) and dopamine. It is these neurotransmitters which antidepressant medication homes in on, as research has shown that levels of these chemicals are often lower than normal in people suffering from depression. (For more about how these drugs work, see Chapter 4.)

In postnatal depression, however, changes in hormone levels after childbirth may also act as a trigger. As already mentioned in Chapter 1, imbalances in the thyroid hormones after birth account for around 10 per cent of women who suffer postnatal depression. Other hormones for which there is evidence of a link are the female hormones oestrogen and progesterone, and the stress hormone cortisol.

Oestrogen and Progesterone: The Female Hormones

Oestrogen and progesterone are responsible primarily for regulating the female reproductive cycle. Oestrogen is usually present in tiny amounts in the body throughout the cycle, rising slightly around ovulation and then dipping in the run-up to menstruation; progesterone levels rise dramatically around ovulation and then fall back to next to nothing in the approach to menstruation.

As soon as an egg has been fertilized, these hormones are galvanized into action to ensure that the pregnancy takes hold: oestrogen is needed for the fertilized egg to mature; progesterone ensures the egg implants into the lining of the womb, and thereafter keeps the pregnancy going. Levels of both hormones remain high during pregnancy; progesterone, for example, is around 50 times higher during pregnancy than it peaks during the normal menstrual cycle.

Immediately after the birth, however, levels of these hormones drop drastically as the body goes into a resting phase allowing it time to recuperate. During this phase a woman does not ovulate. It can take around six to eight weeks from the birth for menstruation to return; if a woman breastfeeds fully, this resting phase lasts until breastfeeding stops. Hormonally, it means that oestrogen and progesterone remain very low in the body throughout this phase, only reaching their pre-pregnancy levels once the woman starts ovulating again.

These female hormones appear to have an effect on our mood. Changes in oestrogen levels in the premenstrual period, for example, have been associated with the depression and irritability of premenstrual syndrome (PMS). Many women find that taking oestrogen supplements helps to overcome these unpleasant symptoms, and hormone replacement therapy can help women going through the menopause when production of the female hormones drops off.

Of particular interest is a recent British trial (1) which used oestrogen successfully to combat postnatal depression in the first 12 weeks after delivery. Women with early-onset depression were chosen particularly because it is more likely at this stage that depression is linked to hormonal upheaval. This is one of the first trials looking into this approach, so the results are preliminary; we are still some way from being routinely offered oestrogen for postnatal depression, especially since the problem does not appear to be hormonally triggered in all cases.

With regard to progesterone, it has been suggested that the high levels of progesterone in the body during pregnancy are linked to the feelings of serenity women often experience at this time. Research has found that progesterone can block the production of monoamine oxidase, the brain enzyme responsible for breaking down feel-good neurotransmitters like serotonin and noradrenaline (norepinephrine); by blocking monoamine oxidase, more feel-good chemicals are left circulating in the brain.

Much of the work into the role of progesterone in postnatal depression has been undertaken by Dr Katharina Dalton, a British expert on this approach to both premenstrual tension and postnatal depression. She uses progesterone preventively for women who have suffered postnatal depression with a previous baby. The treatment is given by injection followed by progesterone suppositories, and starts immediately after delivery of the placenta. In her seminal book, *Depression After Childbirth*, Dr Dalton gives full details about progesterone treatment and, drawing on several studies, claims a 90–92 per cent success rate in stopping recurrence of postnatal depression in subsequent pregnancies. The medical profession remains unconvinced about progesterone treatment, however, although there are some independent studies which show possible links. In one study, for example, published in the *British Medical Journal* (2), researchers found that women with the highest prenatal and lowest postnatal levels of progesterone were more likely to suffer from the baby blues in the days following the birth.

Cortisol: The Stress Hormone

This hormone is produced by the adrenal gland and is responsible for keeping blood pressure and blood sugar levels – and hence energy levels – on an even keel, as well as boosting the body's ability to cope with stress. Research has found that in late pregnancy, levels of cortisol and another cortisol-releasing hormone are much higher than normal, as the body prepares for the stress and rigour of labour. After delivery, levels of cortisol drop drastically while the body regulates itself – and low levels of cortisol are associated with depression. Although there is not sufficient evidence at present to say firmly that cortisol plays a role in postnatal depression, it is possible that the baby blues and early-onset depression are triggered by lack of this hormone, combined with the other hormonal swings.

SOCIAL ASPECTS OF POSTNATAL DEPRESSION

The changes in our hormonal make-up during pregnancy and just after the birth have always occurred as part of the natural process of childbirth so it is not enough to explain why postnatal depression should be a growing problem now. What has changed over the past 50 years or so is the social situation in which women are becoming mothers. Increasingly, experts in the field are looking at a new mother's social circumstances for answers as to why one woman develops postnatal depression and another does not, and they have come up with the following factors which appear to exert a strong influence in causing postnatal depression.

Lack Of Support

Women can become very isolated nowadays and it is thought that this isolation is a major contributor to the growth in rates of postnatal depression. It cannot be coincidence that it is highly industrialized countries which have a growing problem, barring Japan, where its incidence is low. But in Japan, it is still customary for a new mother and baby to spend the first months after the birth with her mother. Immediately the new mother has support, company and an open-door into a traditional system that has worked well for new mothers for centuries.

In the past, women grew up around babies in a way we do not nowadays – unless you come from a large, close family. Girls were surrounded by the offspring of aunts, sisters and cousins from a young age; they saw babies being breastfed and watched mothers cope with crying babies and survive sleepless nights; they were also expected to babysit themselves when needed and older sisters often shared in the care of younger siblings with a busy mother. Because of this, girls were at ease around young children and had a first-hand view of different ways of parenting. Then, when a woman had her own baby, her mother and other female relatives were on hand to help through the first weeks, months and years, and fathers could – and did – take a backseat with childcare.

Today we are more mobile: couples move away from their home town to find better jobs or housing and end up having only each other for support after the birth. Even if you still live near close family, the chances are that mothers, aunts and sisters will be busy working. There is a tendency, too, now to guard our privacy jealously: baby problems like crying, illness and sleepless nights are coped with in a vacuum, tucked away from outsiders' eyes by a couple who may have very little experience of dealing with a baby.

Jan's experiences as a new mother highlight the shifts that have taken place in our lives:

'I had a busy social life until my son Darry came along,' she remembers. *'I worked in insurance as a customer adviser and was used to*

meeting people, chatting, lunching and so on. All that changed. I was stuck at home, my family were 60 miles away, I really knew no one and I hadn't struck up a friendship with anyone at my antenatal classes.'

Jan soon realized where they lived wasn't ideal for someone at home all day with no car, looking for entertainment for a small baby:

'The fact that it was a quiet residential area on the outskirts of town was a plus point when we bought the house, but it wasn't once we had Darry. It was a good 50 minutes' walk from the town centre and buses were few and far between. It had a corner shop, a handkerchief-sized "park" and mile upon mile of new housing. I'd walk those streets with the pram feeling frustrated and bored out of my mind, wishing I was back at work.'

Jan became very depressed, and angry, at her situation:

'. . . although I really bottled up the anger. I felt I didn't have a life of my own, that I had become grey and uninteresting. I couldn't be bothered to do anything – even getting dressed in the morning was an effort so I'd sometimes go all day in my dressing gown. I did go to the clinic but that was because I was frightened they might suspect there was a problem if I didn't. I was resentful of my husband Derek, because he seemed to have it all. He had the car, he had work and he got out of the house and met people. I didn't get angry or shout at him, though – the opposite in fact. I could hardly bring myself to talk and listen to him, or look at him, and I certainly didn't want him touching me. Our sex life dried up completely.

When Darry was six months old, I went back to work. It hadn't been part of the original plan, but I knew I had to go back. I felt very confused because I wanted to be with Darry but I also knew I'd be a better mother if I had some space to myself. It still took time to overcome my depression, because I felt guilty about not being at home with him, but I made the right choice. I think returning to work saved me – and my marriage.'

The people we are most likely to turn to for advice and company are, of course, our family. But help and support can come from other directions, too: from friends, from other mothers with young children, from supportive health professionals, the mother and baby clinic, or from clubs for parents with young children. It can also come through your church or place of worship, or from neighbours and others in your local community. If you have a good relationship with your partner's family, it can come this route, too.

> *'I hadn't had much to do with Nick's family before the baby arrived'* says Pat, *'but Nick's mum stepped in when my own mother couldn't and she was brilliant. She knew not having a clean house bothered me, so she'd come around and tidy, vacuum and wash-up, while I rested. The other thing I liked was that she didn't interfere – just helped. So when I became a bit depressed, I turned to her for a shoulder to cry on.'*

But by far and away the most important support person is your partner. Although most men now wish to get involved in babycare, regrettably there are still many new fathers who feel that it is the woman's job; there are even some who will help only grudgingly with housework. As one mum admits:

> *'I don't believe he's ever changed a nappy. He just tells me the baby's "done something". He doesn't cook. He doesn't clean. He doesn't get up at night. His attitude is that he works at work and my job is the house and the baby. Then he wonders why I'm depressed.'*

Lack Of A Confiding Relationship

Part of supporting the new mother is being there when she needs to open up about her problems, and in this it seems the most significant person is her partner – because the mother knows that this person is as involved emotionally and has as much invested in the situation as she has. Not having this kind of confidante is another high risk factor in developing postnatal depression – identified in single mothers and in those partnerships going through relationship difficulties.

Having a newborn baby is emotionally hard work and, with your first baby, you are also learning how to be a mother. You are continually second-guessing your baby's needs and ministering to them. If the baby cries and nothing you do seems to pacify her, then you often feel that you are not meeting those needs, although desperate to do so. Crying is one of the most fraught areas: in the early days a baby can cry as if in pain and often nothing you do can stop her crying or ease her seeming discomfort. It is at these times that mothers often need someone else they can turn to for confirmation that everything is all right or – if there appears to be a problem – to help make the decision to call a doctor.

Babycare is also a 24-hour job which can bring with it a lot of frustration, despondency and even boredom. Because of this, new mothers need to open up to someone about their inner-most feelings, to feel able to say, 'I felt very down today. The baby cried for most of the morning and then brought up her feed all over the carpet. I was worried something was wrong and felt I wasn't doing anything right'. Very often this may mean talking about feelings a mother perhaps feels ashamed of – like anger towards the baby, frustration, hopelessness, guilt – and she needs to be able to talk these feelings through without being judged for having them.

But being there emotionally is something many men are uncomfortable with. They are not used to talking through emotional problems and tend to approach a confiding conversation by giving advice:

'I stopped going to Tony if I felt down,' says mother-of-two Elaine. *'He always felt he had to find a solution and tell me what to do. But his advice was so pat and far removed from the actual day-to-day reality of being with the children.'*

Sometimes, too, the new father is not willing to give the backup emotional support his partner is crying out for.

'Jack had been working all week including Saturday. Then he announced he was going to play golf on Sunday, which I knew

meant he'd be away all day,' remembers Jane of the early weeks with daughter Holly. *'He seemed to have no idea how I felt – I think he believed I was having a good time at home, doing "nothing" all day. But I'd been almost literally tearing my hair out waiting for Sunday just so I'd have someone to share the baby with, so that it wouldn't all be down to me. When he said about the golf, I felt like scratching his eyes out.'*

Financial Difficulties

Having money worries depresses everyone, but having a new baby to cope with as well can quickly tip the scales towards postnatal depression. Becoming parents often brings with it financial constraints because suddenly the family income is halved. In some unfortunate instances, the new father may already be unemployed or is made redundant around the time the baby is born – a double blow to the new family, which also increases the likelihood of the father becoming depressed.

It is often said that babies are expensive, and it is true that they need a lot of basic equipment from clothes and nappies to a pushchair, cot and car seat, and that is before you even take stock of all the other paraphernalia that manufacturers would like to convince you are necessary for the modern baby. We all want the best for our baby and it can be difficult seeing others laden down with new equipment if you cannot afford the same for your new-born. This puts a strain on both the family budget and your feelings of self-worth and, in the end, can cast a shadow over actually enjoying your baby. However, it is worth remembering that it is possible to obtain good quality secondhand equipment for only a fraction of the brand-new price. Scan the small ads in newspaper and ask around, too.

Financial worries may also mean that the father has to work longer hours, and recent surveys tend to bear out this fact: one UK survey found one in four fathers with a young family put in over 50 hours a week (3). In addition, most employers still do not look with a friendly eye upon paternity leave (in some companies, it is almost seen as a lack of commitment to the job), so most new fathers take one or two weeks' holiday after the birth and then go back to work. For self-employed men, the father may not be able to afford to take time off. Inevitably, this means that right from the start the new mother finds herself left alone at home for long periods, shouldering most of the babycare problems and worries.

Since new mothers spend so much time in the house, it is unsurprising to find that there is a strong association between poor housing and postnatal depression. If you are stuck in cramped living conditions – perhaps dealing with problems like inadequate heating, damp, mould and pest infestation – with no garden and very little outside your front door to tempt you and the baby out, then it can be difficult not to become frustrated and despondent.

Relationship Difficulties

Since your partner is so central to your needs for support and emotional confiding, it stands to reason that existing fissures in that relationship will increase the likelihood of postnatal depression. It can also exacerbate feelings of low self-esteem, guilt and anger. These kind of difficulties go beyond the 'he does nothing in the house' frustrations; this is where the relationship has lost its close connection and is in danger of breaking down.

Sometimes these problems were there before the baby came along and the pressures of caring for a newborn bring them to the surface. It may be that the baby was an attempt to rescue the relationship, although this seldom works because having a newborn actually increases the strains. Relationship difficulties can also develop after the baby is born, for a range of reasons. In some cases, the new father feels jealous because his partner is so preoccupied with the baby that there seems no room for him: 'She's completely involved with the baby. I'm shut out,' said one father.

Sex is often a contentious area where many of our insecurities come to the fore. A woman may worry that, after seeing her give birth her partner may no longer find her sexually attractive. She may worry, too, that her body may feel different to her partner during sexual intercourse. It takes time for the body to get back to its pre-pregnancy shape and any stretch marks and weight gain may also make a woman feel self-conscious about her body.

Largely, however, it is other reasons which make new mothers lose interest in sex. In the weeks after the birth, most women's bodies are not physically ready for intercourse. Later, tiredness takes its toll. As Elaine succinctly puts it:

> *'I was dog-tired for the first four months because Danny was such a poor sleeper. When I went to bed, all I wanted to do was sleep.'*

In addition, one of the symptoms of depression can be loss of libido, and even if you are only mildly depressed, you may not be bothered with sex. This can cause conflict in a relationship, particularly if the father is feeling insecure about his place and role now that the baby is here. Some men also find it difficult to reconcile the idea of his partner as a lover with also being a mother.

With postnatal depression, new fathers can play an important role in tipping the balance one way or the other. It can seem a heavy burden for the new father at a time when he, too, is finding his feet, but it highlights that fact that men are certainly not bystanders in the family; they are intrinsic to its wellbeing and development into a happy, cohesive unit; and they are much needed by their partners at a challenging stage in their lives.

Depression In Pregnancy

Many health professionals believe that antenatal depression is a common but underestimated problem, with several studies finding that a high percentage of women who report being depressed in pregnancy go on to develop postnatal depression. In these cases, postnatal depression may be part of an on-going problem with depression.

If you become depressed while pregnant, it is vital to seek help from your doctor quickly so the problem can be treated. Treatment will depend on how depressed you are but it is most likely that you will be offered counselling or psychotherapy. If you do need antidepressants, your doctor will choose ones least likely to affect the baby and put you on the lowest dose possible to control your symptoms. There are also many complementary or alternative therapies which you can try. But it is important that you have a proper consultation and that you do not self-medicate in pregnancy.

If you opt for psychotherapy it may be wise to carry on with psychotherapy after the baby is born. Your doctor may also prescribe antidepressants postnatally in conjunction with psychotherapy, and will follow your postnatal progress closely.

YOU, THE INDIVIDUAL

Finally, there are the personal and individual triggers for postnatal depression, those aspects which depend on your background and psychological make-up. Perhaps the most important factor here is whether there is **a history of depression in your family** and whether **you have suffered from depression in the past**. Other indicators which also appear to be significant are as follows.

Complications during pregnancy, labour and in the immediate postnatal period The chances of postnatal depression rise if you have a less than straightforward pregnancy, a traumatic labour and health problems just after the birth.

Complications in pregnancy include threatened miscarriage, pre-eclampsia, premature birth and low-birthweight baby. These problems can cause the mother to suffer much anxiety and stress throughout the pregnancy, which may develop into antenatal depression, or later as postnatal depression.

Difficult labour includes being induced and deliveries resulting in interventions, for example use of forceps and particularly Caesarean section. One study of depressed mothers in the UK found that around 55 per cent had an obstetric intervention of one sort or another.

Particularly why this should prompt postnatal depression is not clearly understood, although it could be that a birth involving medical intervention often takes longer to recover from physically than an unaided birth. On the psychological side, many women feel they have failed if they do not manage to give birth 'naturally', without medical intervention. There is also the question of control: if the birth becomes highly medicalized, the labouring woman may feel that doctors have taken over her body and the care of her baby. Many women talk about feeling out of control when this happens in their labour and it may prompt a spiral of feeling not able to cope. In this way, women take with them into motherhood feelings of failure, anxiety, even humiliation and anger, which may trigger depression later when faced with the day-to-day problems of life with baby.

Although efforts are being made to cut down the rates of intervention in delivery, many health professionals and campaigners believe it still occurs far too frequently and is not always in the best interest of the mother or the baby. Caesarean rates – which stand at around 15 per cent of births in the UK and 22 per cent in the USA, where it is the most commonly performed surgery – are a particular cause for concern.

Health problems after the birth can include mastitis, uterine infection, sore and/or infected stitches, haemorrhage (heavy blood loss), pelvic pain, and anaemia. Unfortunately, these physical problems coincide with the peak time for the baby blues and tiredness is also beginning to take its toll. It is likely that this combination could tip susceptible women into full-blown depression.

Adjustment Problems

Once upon a time women married young and once married they didn't work outside the home and children came along fairly quickly. Nowadays, the trend is to settle down later, after you have enjoyed single life fully and, in many cases, established a career. Even after settling down, many of us tend to wait before starting a family until we are financially comfortable. Generally in the West, there has been an increase in the number of women between 25 and 40 years old having babies, and a corresponding dip in the 20 to 24 age group.

This trend is significant in any discussion of postnatal depression because it has a bearing on how well a woman will cope with the great life change that is motherhood. By the time you are in your thirties, you are used to being in control of your life. Then the baby comes along and – however organized you are – that control is difficult to maintain. The reality of life with baby can throw parents completely off balance as you struggle to maintain some semblance of your previous life. Of course, we can't do this, and perhaps, trying to exacerbates any depression. Things will *not* be the same, and why should they?

So, in many ways, postnatal depression may be a kind of mourning for what has been lost, especially if you are finding it difficult to come to terms with yourself as a mother.

'I remember standing at the bedroom window, watching the college kids go by while I tried to stop Danny crying,' says mother-of-two Elaine. *'I was crying hopelessly myself because I had a baby now and I'd never be as free as those school kids again.'*

At a very fundamental level, becoming a parent changes the inner you, and this, too, can be part of the challenge which creates conditions for postnatal depression. Motherhood shapes your hopes and dreams for the future; it turns your ideas on what is important in life upside-down; it sensitizes you to violence and cruelty; it makes you fearful, not for what life might throw at you, but what it might throw at your children. It plays havoc with your emotional life and, although in the beginning this might be linked to changing levels of hormones, the effects are too long-lasting for it to be purely a chemical reaction.

Motherhood turns you into something strange, new and vulnerable. Hard-headed businesswomen turn into emotional mush at a phone call from the nanny or childminder telling them their two-year-old has a throat infection; ex-Schwartzenegger addicts are suddenly unable to watch the news because all the violence and horror seems too personal. Next time you are at the park and a child falls and screams, watch all the mothers look around. Parents are easy to spot.

Your Relationship With Your Mother

There does appear to be a connection between how well you are able to adjust to being a mother and communicate with your baby and your relationship with your own mother. Research has shown that, from a few hours old, mother and baby have started to establish communication with each other but in cases where the mother has postnatal depression, this communication can be difficult. This is discussed in more detail in Chapter 3, but suffice to say here that this inability to communicate can stem from not having a good role-model yourself when growing up to show you how to be a mother. It has been found, for example, that losing a mother before the age of 11 can affect mothering abilities. Certainly, loss of parents at a young age is strongly associated with depression later in life.

Even if a woman had her mother around as she was growing up, it might be that the mother was not a good role model for motherhood. Perhaps there was a lack of closeness in the relationship, or the mother was unsympathetic, even hostile, towards her child, rejecting her. It may also be that the new mother was abused by her parents as a child and has grown up with a distorted view of parenting. Meeting her new baby's needs with this background may be painful for a new mother.

The sex of the baby can prove a problem as well. In some cases, it may be that the mother feels a boy baby is alien to her, or he may bring back memories of abuse; a girl baby may create unlooked-for feelings of conflict and jealousy in the new mother, especially if she had a bad relationship with her own mother.

Feelings About The Pregnancy, Or A Former Pregnancy

Sometimes, if the pregnancy was unwanted, this can lead to feelings of guilt or anger which in turn lead to depression. Even if the baby is much wanted, postnatal depression can also set in because the baby brings back memories of a baby who was lost, for example, an abortion for whatever reason, miscarriage, stillbirth or cot death. These events are painfully traumatic and coming to terms with the death of a baby takes a long time. Having a new baby will bring memories and feelings to the forefront again, along with anxieties about her safety and wellbeing.

For many of these individual triggers for postnatal depression, psychotherapy or counselling is indicated to help work through the painful, and perhaps conflicting, feelings. What is important to remember is that we come to any relationship – with a lover, a friend or our own children – with emotional and psychological 'baggage' attached. It is how we carry that baggage that signifies how well the relationship will develop. In postnatal depression you need to ensure there is a smooth flow of emotion and communication between all members of the new family: mother and father, mother to baby, and vice versa. Psychotherapy can certainly help you to understand the emotional baggage you bring with you and work through the problems it creates, and in this way postnatal depression can be beaten.

Risk Factors For Postnatal Depression

A worthwhile exercise might be to assess whether any of the following are at the root of feelings of depression and what can be done to lessen their effects. Some of the self-help suggestions and strategies in this book will help, but talking to a sympathetic health professional who will be able to guide you towards treatment is also important.

- previous depression, or a strong family history of depression
- depression or anxiety in pregnancy
- problems during the pregnancy or in the immediate postnatal period
- unplanned pregnancy
- being a single mother
- traumatic labour or one which involved medical intervention
- multiple birth
- a stressful life event around the time of the birth, eg, a death in the family, redundancy of spouse, relationship break-up
- lack of support/isolation
- lack of a confiding relationship, particularly with a partner
- relationship difficulties
- financial problems
- health problems in mother
- problems adjusting to motherhood
- previous miscarriage, stillbirth or cot death

CHAPTER 3

Postnatal Depression and the Family

All forms of depression have an effect on the people around the person who has the illness but postnatal depression can have a more weighty effect for several important reasons. First, the feelings engendered by the depression inevitably impact upon the baby and disrupt communication between mother and baby at a critical time in the baby's development. Postnatal depression also hits the woman's partner particularly hard, because it occurs at a time of transition for him, too. Lastly, it will affect any older children in the family.

HOW YOU FEEL

As already outlined in Chapter 1, the postnatal period has a number of physical symptoms like weight and appetite fluctuations, fatigue and insomnia, which are also features of postnatal depression. But depression is primarily about feelings: how you feel about yourself, your circumstances, the people around you, your life. Obviously, the most constant feeling is one of dejection, of feeling down, 'like sitting at the bottom of a black hole', as one mother put it. Other mothers describe their depression like this:

'Everything was an effort, a grind, just to get myself onto my feet and move.'

'Nothing seemed worth doing. I felt why bother, it won't change anything.'

'I felt like I had a dark, heavy cloud in my head that stopped me thinking straight and weighed down my whole body.'

'All those things I'd imagined myself doing as a new mother with a summer baby – walks in the park, picnics on the lawn, pushing the pram down the shops – I couldn't muster up the interest to do. We just stayed in, with me feeling like I was going mad.'

This sense of dejection and lack of pleasure can make you feel that somehow your 'good' emotions have gone to sleep and a vast sea of negativity has swamped and over-whelmed you. This can lead to feelings of emptiness, hopelessness, of being unlovable, and of guilt because you can no longer take an interest in those around you, even your children. Says Patricia of her early weeks with her baby:

'It was an effort to do even basic stuff, let alone play with her, but how could I tell anyone that I didn't want to care for Nicola?'

But postnatal depression is a multifaceted illness and there is a range of other emotions that comes with it and which may be part of your experience.

Frustration

This is often a part of postnatal depression and may stem from high ideals and then being unable to meet them – something first-time mothers are apt to do. We want to be the perfect mother, but it is a goal almost certainly doomed to failure – because of our unrealistic expectations of how things will be. We then become disappointed and frus-trated because we cannot live up to our high ideals:

perhaps breastfeeding does not go smoothly, or the baby won't stop crying, and the household chores scream to be done. Or perhaps we are disappointed in ourselves when we lose our tempers, or shout, or break down in tears, because we are not the mature, calm, all-accepting mother we had pictured ourselves as being.

Frustration will be expressed in a number of ways: at the baby and his constant needs; at a partner for not helping enough, or not doing things as we would like them done; at ourselves, for being unable to meet the baby's needs or keep in control, and for not maintaining our (high) ideal. Sometimes that frustration does not even have a definite cause; it is just a general, all-enveloping seething inside.

'I felt so frustrated being stuck in the house all day.'

'Why didn't anyone tell me it was going to be like this; I had no idea!'

'I'd just finish changing his nappy ready to go out and he'd either do a really horrible poo, throw up or something, and I'd have to start all over again. You feel like screaming, because you know you've just missed the only bus that hour.'

'Doing up car seat harnesses could reduce me to tears on some days, because they just seemed to embody how difficult everything was.'

Anger

This is an emotion that commonly occurs in postnatal depression, but is often camouflaged because new mothers feel so guilty about feeling angry. It is not usually an anger with a clear cause and it often manifests as irritation and snappiness to those around us, particularly other children in the family and partners. Or there may be anger at the baby – for not cooperating, for demanding too much, for crying, for taking over . . .

In postnatal depression, anger often has an element of powerlessness in it: the feeling of being trapped. We are in a situation that we feel unable to change, even though we are unhappy. As Patricia, mother to Nicola, puts it:

'It's like I wanted to give her back and start again when I was more ready, but of course you can't. Once the baby's here, there's no turning back. I felt irrationally angry about being trapped like that.'

It is often also an emotion mothers do not want to admit to because they are ashamed. Not only do we live in a society where expressing anger is generally taboo, but also where any outburst of emotion, especially publicly, is frowned upon. And a new mother is in a situation where she is not supposed to feel emotions, let alone feel angry – she is supposed to feel fulfilled and to glow with fulfilment. So what commonly happens is that the mother turns her anger inwards, leading to feelings of inadequacy, worthlessness and hopelessness. If we start turning anger inwards, it is easy to call one-self names: 'I'm a bad mother', 'I'm so stupid, I can't do anything without messing it up', 'I'm incompetent – what has this baby done to deserve me?'

Anxiety

Many mothers with postnatal depression become overanxious about their baby, worrying obsessively about his health and development:

'I was obsessed with checking Caleb's breathing,' admits Joyce, who suffered from severe postnatal depression in the three months after the birth. *'I was petrified about cot death to such an extent that it overtook everything else. I would sit by his cot and watch him breathing, listening for any changes. I even bought a breathing monitor so I could listen to him in bed. The least little alteration, and I was up and in his room.'*

Doctors and health professionals are often alerted to post-natal depression when they find a mother is bringing her perfectly healthy baby to the doctor or clinic over-regularly about nebulous problems.

Anxiety can also be caused by worries about not doing the job of being a mother well, worries which are exacerbated if the depression is stopping you from responding to the baby.

Low Self-Esteem

Depression inevitably alters the way we think about ourselves. This manifests as feelings of inadequacy, lack of self-worth, self-dislike, inferiority and the notion that we are not good enough.

'I felt she would have done better with any other mother.'

'I looked around and all I saw were other mothers, doing a far better job than I, loving their babies and feeling happy around them.'

This lack of self-esteem creates a vicious circle: a low opinion of oneself and ones abilities, means we become highly self-critical – nothing we do is ever good enough – and this in turn reinforces feelings of inferiority. Sometimes, this can become so bad that we begin to hate ourselves, at which point thoughts of self-harm may set in.

Guilt

This is often a knock-on effect of the other emotions engendered by depression: we feel guilty because we are feeling frustrated, angry or lacking interest in our baby. Guilt also occurs because we feel we are failing the baby: he deserves a good mother and look what he's got, someone who cannot care for him or love him properly, who feels angry at him and frustrated doing things for him . . .

'I knew I should love Betty, but I didn't feel like I did, and I was eaten up with guilt about it.'

'I wasn't caring for her as well as I should have been and I felt guilty.'

'I hid my depression for as long as I could, because I felt so guilty not being able to cope – everyone else seemed to.'

There may also be guilt towards our partner: haven't we smashed his hopes of family life? We lash out at him for no reason; aren't we letting him down? And there are also the social pressures: the guilt we feel because we are not meeting society's – and the media's – expectations of all a mother should be. As a society we have a high expectation of motherhood, of its nurturing, loving, coping and endlessly providing role. If we find nurturing and loving difficult, and find we cannot cope on our own, then it is very easy to feel that we are a failure in some big way.

Thoughts Of Suicide

In any discussion of postnatal depression, the subject of suicide must be covered because so many new mothers experience suicidal feelings. It may only be a passing thought – 'I'm no good for my baby, he would be better off without me' – but sometimes the idea of suicide comes when we hit rock-bottom, when the future looks bleak and unchanging and we feel we will never rise above the depression to become the mother we want to be. When someone becomes this low, it is possible that they might put thoughts of suicide into action.

Even more difficult to contemplate is the act of infanticide, when the mother kills her baby or child. Such cases always receive a lot of media attention when they occur, which tends to cloud the fact that they are extremely rare and only occur when the mother's mind is severely unbalanced – as in cases of puerperal psychosis (see p. 3).

If the mother is deemed psychotic, then mother and baby may have to be separated for a short while, and the mother taken into hospital, until the illness is brought under control and both the mother's safety and that of the baby are assured.

If you are suffering from thoughts of suicide, or your feelings towards your baby are violent and becoming uncontrollable, seek help urgently from your doctor or one of the health professionals known to you. If you are someone close to a mother who is postnatally depressed and she has spoken of suicide or you fear she may be contemplating it, or you are worried for the baby's safety, then suggest she talks to her doctor or a health professional – or ask whether she would mind if *you* did on her behalf.

From the depths of depression, it can be difficult to contemplate tackling all these strong emotions. It is possible to overcome them, however, by working on the way we think about ourselves and our situation – by turning negative thinking into something more positive. There are strategies to help do this in Chapter 5. However, in severe or persistent depression, psychotherapy will be indicated to help develop individual strategies to get these emotions into perspective.

YOUR RELATIONSHIP WITH YOUR BABY

In the past, people tended to think of newborns as passive, inert beings, not aware of anything that was happening around them. We are now just beginning to learn that this is not the case. It appears that a baby right from birth is interacting with his environment and trying to communicate; he is learning how to respond to other people, how to elicit care and how to feel. Because, in most circumstances, it is his mother who is his constant carer, it is through his mother that the baby learns about the outside world and his place in it. His mother is the baby's main cue card for all these aspects of early development. If the mother is not giving the baby the correct cues, or not responding at all – both of which can occur in postnatal depression – then the baby is likely to develop response mechanisms that are slightly awry.

Studies of how non-depressed mothers interact with their babies show that they soon develop a way of 'talking' to each other, by mirroring what the other does, and taking it in turns to 'initiate' communication. The baby will copy his mother's facial movements after she has pulled a face or laughed; and mother in turn, will copy the noises and facial expressions, made by her baby.

If a mother is depressed, this two-way communication is likely to break down. The mother is 'switched off' and does not respond to the baby's attempts to 'talk' to her. This may be because the lethargy and emptiness of depression has left her unable to respond, or because she feels emotionally detached from her baby, unable to cope with the feelings the baby arouses in her. This also means that a mother with postnatal depression may not play much with her baby, may present her baby with a blank face most of the time, is unlikely to smile at her baby, or to always respond to the baby's smiles. In these situations, the baby still learns from his mother, but what he learns is to be sad, and not to bother communicating.

If a mother with depression *does* respond, it may be then that she responds inappropriately: turning away from the baby when he tries to start a conversation, or perhaps responding with hostility or even over-enthusiastically, in an effort to compensate for the lack of feeling she has inside. In severe cases, there may be frank hostility, and this may lead to physical abuse. In these cases, the baby himself will learn inappropriate responses, so that as he grows up he, in turn, may respond with hostility, for example, or over-enthusiastically to other people's friendly overtures.

Babies do devise ways to deal with a lack of response on the part of their main carer. One way is for the baby to give up trying to win his mother's attention and become withdrawn. One study of babies at around three months found that those with depressed mothers protested less when their mothers refused to play with them than babies of non-depressed mothers. Even at such a young age, these babies had already given up. Other studies have asked non-depressed mothers to put on blank faces for their babies, withholding a response for a fixed time. Video tapes of these sessions show the baby reaching out for his mother, then – after receiving no response for a short while – finally turn away, looking sad.

The other way babies cope is by trying harder, becoming hyperactive, in an attempt to gain attention. This hyperactivity will obviously have an effect on the baby's sleeping, feeding and learning patterns, making him a more 'difficult' baby than he might otherwise have been, and so a vicious circle develops: the depressed mother is made more depressed by having a difficult baby, who then tries even harder to gain her attention.

The hyperactive response appears to be more common in boys than girls, girls being more likely to become withdrawn. Boys cry more, are fussier babies and become angrier when their depressed mother does not respond to them. One study found that depressed mothers often also react differently towards sons than daughters, expressing more anger and less joy with boys than girls, which led boys to seem less happy, even at as young as three months old.

There is an increasing amount of research tracing how this communication breakdown between mother and baby affects a child as he grows. This research has tended to find that the children of postnatally depressed mothers:

- often grow up with more negative impressions of their mothers, and feel less secure in their relationship with her, than children of non-depressed mothers;
- have lower self-esteem because they feel their mother is unhappy with them;

- are more likely to suffer from depression and anxiety as children, and from depression and other mental health disorders as adolescents and adults. It is estimated that older children of depressed parents have a three to four times higher than average rate of adjustment problems, like depression, anxiety, phobias, attention deficit disorder and aggressive, disruptive behaviour. Boys are more likely to become aggressive and girls more likely to be anxious;
- suffer more from learning and behavioural difficulties.

Set out baldly like this, these findings appear alarming and need placing in context. Firstly, much depends on the severity of the depression and how long it lasts: the sooner the mother receives medical and/or psychotherapeutic attention and treatment, the more quickly a normal mother/baby relationship can begin. Also, other factors have an effect: for example, it has been found that depressed mothers who have a disrupted relationship with their baby also tend to have more marital and social problems, and these, in turn, would obviously affect the development of the child. So it can be difficult to judge to what extent a child's problems stem solely from his mother's postnatal depression or from the breakdown in his parents' relationship, for example, or his father leaving the family home. The baby's temperament, too, will affect how he reacts to his mother's depression; some babies may be more able to bounce back from the early effects of the mother's depression than others. There are studies which suggest that children of depressed mothers may actually be better at communicating with other adults, because they have grown up assessing their mother's emotional state, which leaves them adept at gauging what others are feeling.

There is also the assumption here that the mother is the only human being in the baby's world who can provide this communication response. But the father – or grandmother, or anyone who can be there consistently for the baby – can step in and provide stimulating, positive, inter-active contact. Even older brothers and sisters have a role to play in communicating with the baby and teaching him how to respond to the world. In this, a family has to be aware of when the mother cannot be there for the baby and when there is a need for someone else to step in. This can be hard to recognize and it may take a health professional like a psychiatric nurse or psychotherapist to assess.

It is also important to remember that babies and chil-dren are resilient creatures. There are many cases where children have suffered from terrible, traumatic beginnings in life – being orphaned, taken into care, deprivation, the effects of war, abuse and cruelty – and still grow into well-adjusted adults. A baby will overcome a faltering start in life as long as he goes on to be part of a caring and secure family.

Becoming 'A Mother'

We tend to think that as soon as the baby is born, we become mothers – but the fact is that, although physically we are mothers, emotionally it takes longer to form a maternal iden-tity, to redefine ourselves as mothers, and feel comfortable with the role. It has been estimated that it can take between 3 and 10 months for a woman to integrate the maternal role into her life. This process of 'becoming a mother' is interwoven with the bonding process – the development of a binding emotional tie between mother and baby – so bonding is more of a dynamic process than an immediate phenomenon – though it can be that too.

FATHERS AND DEPRESSION

In focusing so exclusively on depressed mothers and their babies, it is easy to forget the role of the father in forging the family. As already mentioned in the previous chapter, a woman is very much more likely to develop postnatal depression if she does not have a supportive partner. But men themselves are often emotionally vulnerable at this time. They may be worried about the responsibility they have taken on, insecure about their own role as a father and how the relationship with their partner will change now that there are three in the family. In working out what their role in the family will be, many men look to how the mother is shaping *her* role and adapt accordingly. Fathers appear to bond with their babies later than mothers, and one reason for this may be that they are waiting for the mother to establish her role with the baby and become confident and happy in that role; worry about a depressed mother may mean the father bonds with his baby later than he would normally.

If his partner is depressed and seems to be having difficulties adjusting to motherhood, the new father may feel confused himself about what he is supposed to do. He may feel like a bystander to his wife's depression, knowing that something has gone awry but not sure what exactly, or how to tackle the problem. And like his partner, he may also be coping with the additional strains that come with having a newborn: tiredness, extra responsibility, overwork and anxiety about the baby.

Men can also find it hard to understand why their partner has become depressed. After all, we are brought up to believe that mothering is an almost automatic response on the part of women and a hiccup in that response may cause confusion in the man. In many cases, where the man is not sure what his partner needs from him or where attempts to help are rebuffed, a wedge may be driven between them – especially if there are additional pressures like financial worries or existing relationship difficulties. Many mothers with postnatal depression also become aggressive towards their partner, projecting blame for the situation on to them, and accusing them of not doing enough to help, or of not understanding. This can make the father frustrated, angry, guilty, and depressed also.

Depression In Men

Work carried out in the UK, the United States and in Canada into the effect of postnatal depression on partners has found that a high proportion of men become depressed. One study found signs of depression in 10 per cent of the men whose partners had postnatal depression; another study of mothers taken into a mother and baby unit with severe postnatal depression found that half the men also had problems with depression.

> *'I felt I had failed because Sonia and the baby were taken into hospital,'* admits Douglas of events that happened two years ago. *'It was as if they were being taken away from me because I wasn't able to take care of them well enough. And, yes, I did become depressed. I cried at home, alone, because I felt Sonia and I had lost something we would never get back. But I didn't tell anyone how I felt. I didn't know who to tell and I was embarrassed. I just thought I'd get over it.'*

Men and postnatal depression is not an area that has been the focus of much attention, and what research there is has not answered the question 'What came first: the man's depression or the woman's?'. We do know from studies into general depression that if one partner is depressed, this increases the likelihood of the other half of the partnership also succumbing; it has also been found that the mood of the woman tends to follow that of the man. So, it may be, in some cases of postnatal depression, that the new father was already depressed before the birth and that his depression precipitated the mother's illness.

The area remains unclear partly because like Douglas men do not admit to being depressed. If we look at the statistics, it seems that far more women than men suffer from depression, but many doctors believe that they do not know the extent to which men suffer because they are much less likely to come forward to seek help. As a result, society – and men – continue to view depression as a woman's problem and not something a 'strong man' falls victim to. It is an attitude that needs to be overcome if we are to understand how depression affects men generally, and – specifically in cases of postnatal depression – what effect the man's emotions have on the woman, and vice versa.

OTHER CHILDREN IN THE FAMILY

Women who suffer from depression in a first pregnancy are, unfortunately, more likely to develop it again with a subsequent pregnancy. There is also a proportion of mothers who develop postnatal depression for the first time in a second or later pregnancy; here, circumstances may have changed, leading to more triggers for postnatal depression – for example, starting a second family with a new partner, or a late unplanned pregnancy.

This can mean there are other children in the family apart from the new baby who have to cope with the mother's postnatal depression. The effect it will have on them depends to some extent on their age but undoubtedly confusion is one of the emotional responses to seeing their mother depressed, angry, hostile – or any one of the myriad emotions which accompany the illness. Children cannot understand why their mother is crying and may feel it is something they have done; she may be irritable and unpredictable towards them for no reason they can see, or she may withdraw from them. As already mentioned, the children of depressed parents tend to suffer more mental health disorders, like anxiety, phobias and depression itself; children as young as five can develop anxiety disorders. Again, if the parental relationship is also going through a rocky patch, this can add to older children's emotional burdens.

In response to a mother who is depressed, some children become overanxious and nervous, trying to gauge their mother's mood and respond to it in a way that will please, because, above everything else, children wish to please their parents. In some cases, the child himself becomes like a parent, in that he begins to look after and protect his mother rather than her fulfilling that role for him.

Depressed mothers can also begin to lose hold on their caring role so that, at a practical level, they have difficulty keeping their children properly fed, cleaned and clothed, and the children may also have more accidents and illnesses because they are not supervised well. In some cases, it may be that the school or doctor is alerted to a problem, simply because the children suddenly have these types of problems in what was formerly a well-run family unit.

Other children in the family may place the blame for the mother's depression on the new baby. Most older siblings experience ambivalent feelings when a new baby comes along. Suddenly, after being the sole focus of their parents' attention, they have to share the limelight with a demanding stranger who monopolizes their mother's time and offers nothing to the older child by way of compensation. There is often jealousy and anger, and feelings of hostility can be deepened if the baby appears to be making the mother irritable, unresponsive and unhappy:

> 'Mum got very depressed when my half-brother Victor arrived,' remembers 15-year-old Catie. 'I was 11 when he was born. I hadn't wanted another baby in the family and when Mum became so down, I blamed Victor. It took Mum around a year to get back to normal and in that time I did my best to ignore the fact that he was even in the house. It's taken me a long time to feel that I even like him. But I think he's quite cute now.'

Although children may be affected by a mother's depression, many also manage to sit tight through it and pick up again when the depression is over. A generally secure background, a loving home, a close relationship with the father and other family members, all help to cushion toddlers and children from the effects of the mother's depression.

CHAPTER 4

Finding the Right Treatment

Conventional treatments for postnatal depression are the same as those offered for general depression: antidepressant drugs and/or some form of talking therapy, like counselling or psychotherapy, depending on the severity of the problem. An alternative approach to the problem, is to choose one of the many complementary therapies which can achieve good results in helping with depression.

In the past, treatment for depression has tended to focus on the chemical imbalances in the body which have been implicated in causing depressive symptoms, so antidepressant drugs (to correct these imbalances) used to be the mainstay treatment in the majority of cases. But, as already mentioned in Chapter 2, over the last 20 years or so, it has become increasingly clear that individual circumstances and personality also play a significant role in depression.

Because of this, there has been growing recognition of the fact that, while drugs are often necessary to get quick results, for many people they merely remove the symptoms of the problem: they can help to provide the impetus needed to overcome depression, but that depression is likely to return once the course of medication is completed because the triggers which prompted the depression initially remain firmly in place.

In this, postnatal depression is no different from general depression. Antidepressants can help to get over the lack of motivation and despair which stops so many mothers from actively seeking to get better. But after that, there is a real need to reassess one's role as a mother, to learn coping mechanisms and to change a whole way of thinking to encompass a more positive approach to motherhood and family life. Psychotherapy is a long-term approach, but it aims to get to the roots of the problem(s) and makes depression less likely to return with your next baby.

In fact, a growing body of studies show that psychotherapy or counselling is in many cases all that is needed to help a woman climb out of depression, and, in severe cases, combining it with drug therapy is usually highly effective. What kind of talking therapy a mother receives depends in most cases on the severity of her postnatal depression.

COUNSELLING

This is the first step in 'talking' treatment and is most useful for mild depression. It involves keeping a regular appointment to meet with and talk to a trained counsellor about how you feel, what you are thinking, the problems you are experiencing, your fears and worries. In many cases simply being able to talk to someone outside the immediate situation can help a woman through her depression. Increasingly – and especially in the UK, although other countries have also started similar schemes – health professionals themselves have realized the benefits of letting mothers talk and offer 'listening visits' to those who may be susceptible to postnatal depression, or in whom they see signs that depression may be developing. This entails spending time with a new mother, focusing on the mother's emotional health, allowing the mother simply to talk and offering advice tailored to the individual mother's needs and situation.

If these listening visits are not on offer through your clinic or your depression is deeper, you may be referred by your doctor to a psychiatric nurse counsellor, whom you will see on a regular basis usually at the clinic or local hospital rather than at home. If it appears that the depression could have its roots in problems in the relationship with your partner, then couples counselling may be recommended to help overcome these difficulties and reach a better understanding of each other.

PSYCHOTHERAPY

A mother may be referred to a psychotherapist or clinical psychologist (or she may, of course, refer herself) if the roots of her depression appear to be linked to her feelings about herself or to her patterns of thinking. There are a number of different psychotherapeutic approaches, depending on how the therapist has been trained. For example, supportive psychotherapy would explore the problems and offer encouragement for the mother to solve those problems herself; directive counselling would offer specific strategies to tackle problems; and cognitive behavioural therapy would work towards changing negative or maladaptive thoughts and behaviour. The most common type of therapy offered for depression is cognitive behavioural therapy where the therapist would try to:

- help the mother to recognize negative thinking and show her how to change this to a more constructive thought process
- draw her attention to how critical and bullying she is to yourself and show her how to be kinder, more forgiving, and self-accepting
- teach her how to cope with feelings of anger, guilt and shame

- help her to see how her behaviour and feelings may have their roots in past experiences (for example, in how her own parents treated her as a child).

Meetings may be on a one-to-one basis, or involve a group. Again, if it is the relationship with the mother's partner that is causing difficulties, then marital therapy with the partner may be indicated. If other family members are involved (for example, other children) then there may be a need for family therapy, where the whole family is involved in addressing the problems linked to depression.

Talking therapies obviously involve a commitment to attend appointments and to work with the therapist in order to help oneself – something which may seem difficult if you are very depressed and not receiving any other treatment or support. Talking therapies are not a quick-fix solution to depression; it can take time for results to show, with the number of sessions required depending on the individual. For this reason, psychotherapy is often combined with drug therapy.

'It took me some time to go to the doctor about my depression after Joshua's birth, but I finally dragged myself to the clinic when he was around six months old,' remembers Sally. *'My doctor put me on antidepressants immediately and organized counselling with a psychiatric nurse. I noticed a difference quite quickly with the antidepressants. I felt more capable of doing things, my sleep routine improved and I wasn't as angry and irrational as I had been. But it was the counselling that helped me out of the vicious circle of feeling guilty and putting myself down all the time. I was on antidepressants for around six months but continued with counselling for a year and that really seemed to straighten me out. Ruth, my second baby, is now four months old and there's been no sign of the depression returning.'*

PSYCHIATRIC HELP

In cases of severe postnatal depression or puerperal psychosis, referral to a psychiatrist is most likely as she is a specialist in the field who can assess properly the severity of the illness and decide on appropriate treatment. Treatment is likely to be intensive and may involve attendance at a hospital, at least as a day patient for whole or part of the day, until the condition improves sufficiently. In very severe cases or where there is a danger to either the mother or her baby, hospitalization may be necessary. In hospital, the treatment is basically the same – drug therapy combined with psychotherapy – only it is more closely monitored. If the depression does not seem to respond to any of these treatments, then electroconvulsive treatment (see below) may be recommended.

A hospital stay can in itself be traumatic but it will only be for as long (or as short) as needed to bring the depression under control. The atmosphere is supportive and treatment is closely monitored and tailored to the mother's changing needs.

Electroconvulsive Treatment (ECT)
This approach to treating depression is still used widely throughout the world, but only in severe cases where the illness does not respond to drug therapy and/or psychotherapy, and when the person is hospitalized. According to the campaigning journal *What Doctors Don't Tell You*, it is used on around 20,000 patients with mental health problems in Britain every year, with around 100,000 patients in the USA receiving over half a million treatments a year. It is a very basic approach to altering thought patterns: electrodes are placed on the person's temples or over the front and back of the head and an electric charge is applied to the brain. There is little research into why causing a seizure like this helps counteract depression, but it is thought to work by altering the chemical balance in the brain which in turn helps normalize mood. Treatment usually involves six ECT sessions and the patient is unconscious when it is given. These days, however, ECT is really a treatment of last resort.

DRUG THERAPY

There are several types of antidepressant drug available and they all work in a similar way: by affecting the production of chemicals called neurotransmitters in the brain. There is evidence that, in some cases of depression, levels of these neurotransmitters are lower than normal, so antidepressant drugs simply raise the levels of specific neurotransmitters circulating in the brain.

As these drugs take around two weeks for the levels of chemicals to build up and up to eight weeks before they start working properly, you will not feel any benefits immediately. In addition, they need to be taken continually to maintain the effect, and most doctors recommend antidepressant treatment should last for at least six months to a year. These medicines can also have side-effects (these are listed below under each separate drug type) and the side-effects start straight away, so it is possible to feel worse before feeling better. As tolerance to the antidepressant develops, side-effects should subside.

These drugs, may be prescribed by a family doctor or, if the depression is perhaps not straightforward, then by a psychiatrist after a consultation.

Tricyclic Antidepressants (TCAs)

These work by stopping the neurotransmitter chemicals serotonin and noradrenaline (norepinephrine) from being reabsorbed into the brain cells so there are more of them circulating in the brain. These are the brain chemicals which improve our mood, so, the more of them we have circulating, the better our mood is likely to be. Side-effects include a dry mouth, drowsiness, confusion, constipation, difficulty urinating, blurred vision, increased body temperature, reduced sexual function, sleeplessness, agitation, muscle spasms and tingling in fingers and toes. An overdose of TCAs can be dangerous, producing coma, fits and disturbed heart rhythm.

Monoamine Oxidase Inhibitors (MAOIs)

These may be offered if anxiety is one of your main symptoms. These work by blocking out the enzyme responsible for breaking down serotonin and noradrenaline (norepinephrine), rather than blocking their reabsorption as the tricyclics do. These have side-effects similar to the tricyclics but they also come with dietary restrictions, as they can react badly with certain foods like cheese, red wine and yeast extract as well as medications like decongestants and cough medicines. Taken with these foods they can cause a dangerous rise in blood pressure, headache and vomiting. If you are prescribed a MAOI, your doctor will talk to you about these dietary restrictions and give you a card to take away with you which lists the restricted foods. There is also a newer MAOI available called moclobemide which is safer to take without dietary restrictions.

Selective Serotonin Re-uptake Inhibitors (SSRIs)

These have taken off in a big way since they were launched several years ago, overtaking tricyclic antidepressants in popularity. The most well-known SSRI is undoubtedly Prozac. SSRIs work by increasing levels of serotonin in the brain and, because of this more targeted approach, appear to have fewer side-effects than the older antidepressants. That said, they can still cause visual disturbance, nausea and vomiting, headaches, bowel problems, loss of sex drive, weight loss and increased anxiety.

Lithium

This is primarily a mood stabilizer and may be prescribed for severe depression which involves swings in mood from depression to a hyperactive, manic state. A problem with lithium is that it can be poisonous if levels become too concentrated in the blood; signs of this include blurred vision, vomiting and diarrhoea, and twitching. If you are prescribed lithium, your doctor will want to monitor your blood levels regularly to ensure you are within safe limits.

If you suffer side-effects from an antidepressant which do not abate, then go back to your doctor. Sometimes people try two or three types before they find one which works well. If you cannot find a drug to suit you, you may wish to consider psychotherapy alone as a means of combating your depression or trying psychotherapy combined with an alternative therapy.

None of these antidepressants has been proven safe for use in pregnancy, and many are not recommended during breastfeeding, as traces pass through the mother into breastmilk. If you are breastfeeding and are prescribed antidepressants, your doctor will opt for a drug least likely to affect the baby at normal doses and ensure that you are on the lowest possible dosage for control of your symptoms. She can also advise you on ways to ensure your baby takes in as little of the drug as possible; for example, by timing feeds so that they fall just before you are due to take another dose of the drug, by which time your last dose will

---

Which Drug?
People often confuse antidepressants with a class of drug called benzodiazepines, but these drugs are very different. They are anti-anxiety drugs (tranquillizers) and sleeping pills and are prescribed to overcome feelings of tension, nervousness and panic usually brought on by stress, or to aid sleep. They work in the opposite way to antidepressants, as they cut down on the presence of mood chemicals in the brain instead of increasing them; they are 'downers' as opposed to antidepressants, which are 'uppers'. Because benzodiazepines are highly addictive, they are only given in short courses; antidepressants, on the other hand, are not addictive, so you should not worry that you could become hooked in the same way that people become hooked on tranquillizers like Valium.

be at lower levels in your body. You also, of course, have the option of changing to bottle feeding and should not feel guilty about doing so if you feel it is the safest, most comfortable choice for you and your baby.

COMPLEMENTARY APPROACHES

Nowadays, an increasing number of people visit a complementary therapist on a regular basis. Many now prefer to try a complementary therapy in place of conventional medicine, particularly when conventional treatment involves taking strong drugs with a long list of side-effects, as is the case with antidepressants. They see in complementary approaches a gentler way of fighting depression.

Complementary therapies can be used in either a self-help way – like taking an off-the-shelf remedy or supplement (although this is not advisable if you are pregnant) – or you can see a complementary therapist. Seeing a complementary therapist is your best step if you wish to get over your depression using alternative methods alone; self-help methods can help in mild depression and as an adjunct to counselling, psychotherapy or drug therapy. They can be used in conjunction with conventional treatments, although you should always inform your doctor, psychotherapist and complementary therapist of what you are doing and taking.

What Therapy?

In theory, any complementary therapy should be able to help you get over postnatal depression, but in reality it depends on what you feel comfortable with and what therapists are available in your area. There are some therapies which may not suit you. For example, if you have a needle phobia then acupuncture may not be for you; if you do not like being touched by a stranger, then a touch therapy like massage, aromatherapy or reflexology (foot massage and stimulation) is something you may not feel relaxed with. It is important to bear these things in mind before you make an appointment.

Below is a brief description of some therapies which have a proven track record in helping with depression. It is only a small selection of the therapies on offer, however, and you may know of someone who has been helped by an approach not mentioned here. Personal recommendation is one way to track down a good practitioner; see Finding a Qualified Therapist (p. 60) for more ways to ensure that your therapist is properly trained to treat you.

Homeopathy

This therapy has always placed equal emphasis on the physical and emotional, so it is hardly surprising to find that it can help with depression. Several studies have shown homeopathy can help with typical symptoms of depression like anxiety, anger, resentment, weepiness and lethargy, as well as depression itself. Homeopathy also has a strong counselling approach in that the homeopath encourages you to talk about yourself, your likes and dislikes, your feelings and your past in order to get to the root of your depressive symptoms and decide on an appropriate homeopathic remedy.

Hypnotherapy

This therapy can help in two ways. First, it provides a form of psychotherapy for the patient, allowing her to talk; second, it induces a state of deep relaxation, and this has been shown to help with problems like depression, anxiety and stress. Proper hypnotherapy has little in common with stage hypnosis and the patient is always in control. You will also be taught techniques for self-hypnosis so you can bring yourself to a state of deep relaxation at home in times of immediate need.

Traditional Chinese Medicine

This approach has been used for thousands of years in China to treat any health problem and it can certainly help in cases of depression. Like the majority of complementary therapies, it works towards getting your body back into a state of balance, and views illness as a sign of imbalance in the body. Treatment will be designed to correct these imbalances through the use of herbs, acupuncture, massage and diet with perhaps some gentle exercise, known as t'ai chi qigong. If you do not like the thought of needles, then many practitioners now use laser or electro-acupuncture instead, methods which do not involve having anything stuck into you.

Aromatherapy/Massage

Essential oils have been shown to have a definite effect on mood and the right oils can lift a depressed mood, or calm an over-stressed or anxious mood. Even massage without therapeutic oils can make you feel good about yourself and help in mild cases of depression. In most cases, an aromatherapist makes an individual assessment and decides what mix of oils are appropriate to use in the massage, while also offering oils to burn at home. It is certainly a pampering, feel-good therapy for any mother suffering depression.

'I can't recommend aromatherapy massage enough,' says Pat. 'It was the high point in my week and certainly helped me to combat the bouts of depression after Ben was born. It meant I could spend an hour doing absolutely nothing, with someone taking good care of me for a change, and I'd leave my aromatherapist floating several inches

above the ground. The effect lasted several days and definitely improved my mood.'

Baby massage classes may also be provided. This form of manage is a wonderful way for mother and baby to become closer, especially if there is a problem like post-natal depression. It can help with the bonding process as well as making the mother feel more confident about handling her baby and getting to know what the baby likes, what calms her, what makes her laugh.

Yoga

Yoga is a particularly calming form of therapy and once learnt, can be put into practise anytime. It works on several levels to combat depression: it is relaxing, encouraging deep relaxation and meditation, both of which have been shown to help with depression; it helps regulate breathing, so that breathing becomes more efficient and less shallow and overactive which exacerbates many of the anxiety symptoms of depression; and lastly it provides a gentle form of exercise very suited to women who have just had babies (make sure that your yoga teacher knows you have recently given birth). Yoga is also one of the most easily accessible therapies around – there is likely to be a class already locally – and most classes are not expensive.

Meditation

Since meditation is basically a form of deep relaxation, this too can help with depression. However, to be done successfully, it needs to be taught. Yoga meditation is one method; the others most commonly found in the West are Buddhist and Transcendental Meditation. Transcendental Meditation (TM), the meditation system founded by Maharishi Mahesh Yogi, is actually part of a larger system of natural health care called Maharishi Ayur-Ved which includes a mother and baby programme. Transcendental Meditation requires 15–20 minutes morning and evening to maintain a state of calm and relaxation. Learning yoga and Buddhist meditation is usually quite reasonably priced; TM is more expensive, but once learnt, it is never forgotten and research appears to back up its claims for being able to help treat and prevent a wide range of illnesses, including depression.

Nutritional Therapy

A nutritional therapist differs from a nutritionist or dietitian in that she uses diet to cure health problems and does not just focus on correcting deficiencies. With depression, a nutritional therapist will advise dietary changes and offer supplements to help overcome any deficiencies which may be contributing to the problem as well as boosting your general immunity and mood. She may also check that you are not suffering from a food allergy, which could in some cases be triggering the symptoms of depression, although this is rarely the case with postnatal depression.

COMPLEMENTARY SELF-HELP

Over-the-counter treatments can be of considerable help with mild depression, or if used in combination with conventional or therapist-led treatment. In severe cases of depression, however, always seek outside help for the problem, either from your doctor, assigned health professional or from a qualified complementary therapist. Even in mild cases, a check-up is advisable before trying over-the-counter treatments, and it is best to avoid self-treatment during pregnancy (some essential oils, for example, should not be used when pregnant).

St John's Wort (Hypericum)

This herb – available over the counter as a supplement and found in most health stores and pharmacies – is now much accepted even in conventional circles as an effective treatment for mild to moderate depression. Many studies back up its usage – one of the most influential being a 1996 assessment of 23 studies, published in the *British Medical Journal* (4), which concluded St John's wort was as effective as most antidepressants in treating general depression, but with fewer side-effects. In 1997, it was the first herbal preparation to be recognized and recommended by psychiatrists at the International Congress on Neuropharmapsychology.

It is thought to work like conventional pharmaceutical antidepressants, by boosting levels of noradrenaline (norepinephrine), serotonin and dopamine, but it appears to do so in a less invasive way. It is effective used in conjunction with counselling or psychotherapy and can also be taken with all classes of antidepressant except MAOIs, where it can be dangerous if the two are mixed. It has few side-effects – the main one being gastrointestinal upsets, so it is best taken with meals. Follow the manufacturer's instructions on dosage, although the usual recommended therapeutic dose is 900 mg a day.

Elaine read an article about St John's wort and thought she would try it when she became depressed after her first baby.

> 'I didn't think I was depressed enough to see a doctor and didn't fancy the idea of taking antidepressants, either. After taking the supplement for about three weeks, I began to notice a difference in myself. I had more patience, didn't feel so lethargic and actually found I was making plans to do things with the baby! Now I take it to help me through my PMS mood changes – it really works.'

Essential Oils

As already mentioned under Aromatherapy (see p. 54), essential oils can have a distinct effect on our moods and have been used successfully in trials to combat depressive states. They can be used for massage, in burners or as room sprays, and in the bath.

Using Essential Oils

For massage: use a ratio of 4–6 drops of essential oil to about 2 tsp of a base oil like almond or wheatgerm, depending on how much you wish to mix up.

In a burner: put 2–3 drops of essential oil with a little warm water into the saucer of the burner and light the candle underneath; make sure your burner has a deep saucer and watch that the water does not dry out. You can also buy vaporizers, where you simply drop 2–3 drops of essential oil into the vaporizer.

To make a room spray: half-fill a plant spray with water, add around 50 drops of oil, shake well and spray. Remember to shake before every spray to mix the oils into the water.

In the bath: dilute 4–8 drops of essential oil in 2 tsp of a base oil and add to your bathwater, mixing it around before you get in.

It is better to buy 'essential oils' rather than 'aromatherapy oils': an essential oil should be pure plant extract; an aromatherapy oil will already be mixed with a base or cheaper oil. Store oils in a cool, dark place and keep out of the reach of children. Do not take internally or put neat on the skin – these oils are strong and very potent.

Good Oils For Depression

Basil Balancing oil; good for nervous conditions, anxiety and mental exhaustion. Always dilute well.

Bergamot Tonic for the nervous system, gentle and soothing.

Clary sage One of the great antidepressant oils, excellent for nervous tension, stress and nervous complaints.

Frankincense Calming, stress-relieving oil; burn this oil while meditating or relaxing.

Geranium Another balancing oil, this calms and refreshes; good for anxiety.

Lavender One of the most versatile essential oils, it calms and relaxes and helps with insomnia, stress, tension and depression.

Mandarin Calming, soothing, used for stress, tension and insomnia.

Melissa Another good antidepressant oil which can also help with insomnia.

Rose with insannia Good antidepressant and nerve tonic; also recommended for problems like PMS and painful periods.

Rosewood Mild, calming nerve tonic, good for stress.

Vetivier Another oil with a reputation for helping with depression, insomnia, stress and nervous conditions.

Ylang ylang Calming effect on the nervous system, so good for stress-related problems as well as anxiety and panic attacks.

Note
Do not use at all in pregnancy: basil, clary sage, rose.

Flower Essences

These are aimed at helping emotional problems by altering negative states of mind. They can either be taken to alleviate 'emergency' emotional situations – for example, shock – or for a long-standing emotional or physical disturbance. They are made by distilling the essence of flowers. You will find a range of remedies available in health stores including Australian, South African, Dr Bach and Healing Herbs Flower Remedies.

Bach remedies particularly recommended for depression

Agrimony if you feel overwhelmed by worries.

Gentian if you are depressed by difficulties and setbacks.

Holly for anger and resentment.

Honeysuckle for sad memories and looking back.

Larch if you feel inferior/unappreciated, hopeless.

Pine if you feel you have failed in some way or feel guilty.

Star of Bethlehem for shock.

Wild oats if life seems without direction.

For exhaustion, try **elm**, **hornbeam**, **oak**, or **olive**.

The remedies can be mixed together (up to five) if you have more than one of the emotions described above. Books on flower remedies are widely available and make excellent reading. Flower remedies are totally safe.

Finding A Qualified Therapist

The field of complementary health is still largely unregulated, so there are steps you should take to ensure you receive quality complementary healthcare from an appropriately trained individual.

If your doctor is open to complementary approaches, ask if he can recommend a local practitioner. If not ask other health professionals you know who may have more contact with other mothers who have tried complementary therapies, or find someone you know who can recommend an alternative practitioner.

If you have decided to try a complementary approach but do not have any contacts, you can start looking in one of two ways: either decide which therapy you would like to try, approach the self-regulating body for that therapy (see Useful Addresses, p. 116) and ask for their register of practitioners. Alternatively, you can look through the local phone book. Approach two or three therapists and check out their qualifications, training and fees before deciding. Ensure that the practitioner is a member of the self-regulating body for her therapy; phone the relevant organization to ensure she is on their register (do not take her word for it).

Lastly, do you feel comfortable with the practitioner? She may be fully qualified and experienced in treating depression, but if you do not hit it off then it may affect how well treatment works. Remember that the complementary approach usually means longer appointments and a lot more talking than in conventional medicine and you will also be opening up about emotional matters.

CHAPTER 5

Looking After Yourself

One of the biggest problems we face when we are very depressed is summoning the motivation to take steps to overcome the illness. It is a Catch-22 situation: we need help because we are depressed, but the depression stops us from seeking help or taking steps to help ourselves. In this situation, professional help is required, and a visit to the doctor is essential. Once the depression becomes manageable then self-help becomes more feasible. Some of the suggestions outlined below will help you develop a more positive perspective. Certainly, trying something is one hundred times better than doing nothing at all, even if that 'something' is simply seeking help.

CHANGING THE WAY WE THINK

In the throes of depression, we feel that there is nothing good or enjoyable in the world and so there is no point in trying to seek out something pleasurable. Even once we move beyond this nihilistic stage, it is often hard to get back into the habit of thinking positively, and we are more likely to see ourselves as failures and apply labels, such as 'bad mother', 'useless', 'unable to perform the simplest job', and so on. Then we start to assume that other people see us in the same light.

Because this kind of thinking has a powerful effect on consolidating depression, it is necessary to change these negative thought patterns, into positive ones. This is exactly what psychotherapy aims to do, but there are many self-help steps which can put be into action along the way. This will help you to start thinking positively, to find and accept enjoyment again and start caring for yourself in a way you may not have done for many months.

When negative thoughts occur do not dwell on them. Get into the habit of alerting yourself to negative thinking and then intercepting it and asking yourself how helpful this line of thought is to you. If it is not helpful, then shove it aside and think of something positive; do not let it go around in your head, dragging you down.

When over-critical try to be rational. For example, if the baby will not stop crying, you may find yourself saying: 'Nothing I do ever stops him crying'. Stop yourself there and analyse that statement: is it *really* true that nothing you do ever stops him crying? Then put it in context: 'It is true that, on this occasion, nothing I have done has stopped him crying'. Try to generalize it: 'All babies cry inconsolably sometimes. I'm just feeling frustrated now because I can't calm him down'. And lastly, give yourself a plan of action: 'If I can't stop him crying now, I can stay calm myself and be patient. If it all gets too much, I can put him in his cot and leave him for a few minutes while I go out of the room and calm myself down. Then I can go back and try again'.

If you believe that people – including those nearest to you – view you in a poor light, assess what evidence you have to prove this and look for alternative reasons why they could be acting in the way they are. For example, if a mother you spoke to at a previous mother and baby group appears to ignore you next time around, you may assume it is due to something you have done and jump to the conclusion that she does not like you: perhaps you think you bored her last time, or upset her in some way. Now look for evidence that bears out this view: did you insult her in anyway? Did she seem unfriendly or offended when you parted? Did you have a long conversation in which she could have become bored? Then look for alternative reasons for her not approaching you this time: perhaps she is shy and worried about approaching you first; she may be preoccupied with her baby, who seems a little tetchy; she looks tired – she may have had a broken night last night; or she may simply not feel like talking today. What this analytical reasoning helps you to do is to see that there are many reasons why people react the way they do and those reasons and reactions do not necessarily revolve around you.

Do not try to do it all. If you set high ideals for yourself (and we all do), it is easy to fall into the trap of thinking you have failed if you do not manage everything. Prioritize what you have to do each day and let things drop off the end of the list, if everything is too much for you. If you have a difficult day with the baby, concentrate on him and on allowing yourself time to relax and recover, and let the housework go undone. Dinner does not have to be complicated if time is short; something put under the grill at the last moment is just as nutritious as something slaved over for hours.

Do not feel that just because something you did failed, that it makes you a failure as a person or a bad mother. A failed action does not make you a failed person – it just means you did not hit target this time around.

Do not compare yourself with other mothers. Because you are depressed, comparisons will inevitably leave you feeling guilty and inferior. Besides which, we all tend to keep our frustrations, guilts and anger hidden from view so you cannot tell from the outside how well any other mother is coping.

If you have an angry episode, do not waste time feeling guilty or ashamed of your outburst. Apologize to the person involved, then put it behind you.

Have strategies to deal with anger, for example, counting to 10 before speaking, leaving the room, thumping a cushion, relaxation exercises, deep breathing. This will give you a sense of control over your emotions and an outlet for them.

Steps For Others In The Family

If you are close to someone with postnatal depression, you can help them in many ways.

- **Relieve the burden of everyday chores** off her as much as possible; cook a meal, organize the washing, do the weekly shop.
- **Take over with the baby** on a regular basis, so that she can have some time to herself. Make it a regular time if possible, so she can plan ahead. For example, a father home from work could bath and feed the baby, while mother has a rest. If you say to the mother that you are going to take over in this way at a particular time, try not to let her down: this could be even more de-constructive than doing nothing at all.
- **Show appreciation** of what the mother is doing or achieving, even though she is depressed, and draw her attention to how well she is doing. Be specific when you do this, though, as a general comment like 'You're doing very well, dear' will only seem patronizing.
- **Do not withdraw** from her or avoid visiting, because you will only increase her sense of isolation and lack of self-worth.
- **Do not feel guilty** or responsible – especially if you are her partner. Do not feel that the depression is in some way your fault – there are many factors contributing to it. If you feel there is something in your relationship, or something you have done or said, which may be contributing, speak to her about it.
- **Encourage her to see her doctor** or speak to her allocated health professional about her depression, so that she can receive outside support and treatment if necessary.
- **Arrange to do things together**, even with the baby.
- **Encourage her to join a club** like a mother and baby club or local La Leche League group and also find out what activities there are locally for women at home with young children. If you can, go with her to the first few meetings at least, to help her break the ice and feel comfortable.
- **Be a sympathetic listener** – this means letting her talk without butting in, giving your opinion or judging her. You are allowing her to work through her problems, simply by being there, so try only to give advice if it is asked for.

Have goals which are designed to help overcome depression. These goals should *not* be targets like getting your baby to sleep through the night, or doing the vacuuming every day; they should be about building time for you in the day (see below for more on 'me time'), talking calmly to your partner about how you feel, finding time to enjoy your baby without making it a chore, and so on.

Always have one positive thing to do every day, even if it is only small like buying yourself a sandwich, having a scented bath, picking or buying yourself a bunch of flowers or taking a walk in the park with the baby.

It is easy to become bored at home, so ring the changes by doing something every day or failing that, at least two or three days a week. For example, make Monday the time you visit the library, Thursday your day to go to the park, Saturday for visiting Grandma and Grandad. Joining a mother and baby group makes another change in a monotonous routine.

Start a 'positive diary', writing down each day all the good things that have happened to you. These do not have to be big things: buying yourself a treat, walking by a bed of daffodils in the park, laughing at something your baby did are all events which should find their way into your diary. Doing this will help you to pick out the positive in your day rather than dwelling on the negative and, hopefully, will encourage you to notice positive things as they are happening and enjoying the moment there and then.

Try to plan things you can do together with your partner, with or without the baby, depending on whether you can get a babysitter. Even just taking a walk together at the end of each day can give you an opportunity to talk, a way to relax and a chance to enjoy each other's company.

Be creative: try something like knitting, cooking, painting, gardening, writing, playing an instrument, whatever you enjoy or have in the past. Reading poetry may also help: in one British study (5), poetry reduced stress levels and improved the mood of 42 per cent of the depressed individuals taking part.

Stop reading the newspapers or seeing the news on TV. There is usually not much to cheer you up and learning of troubles besetting the wider world will only make it harder for you to develop a positive environment at home, and inside you.

Try pretending happiness sometimes. This may seem like faking it, but many mothers fake happy feelings anyway but often for the wrong reason: because they do not want anyone to know they are unhappy. Decide that you are going to fake positive feelings to help yourself, and you may find you do feel genuinely happier. Smiling, for instance, can actually make you feel better, promoting happy impulses in the brain.

Lastly, be patient with yourself. Getting over depression is not something you can do in a day. It is often a slow climb out of the black hole, so simply make a commitment to enjoy each step towards the light as it occurs without worrying about when it will all be over and you will be well.

EATING WELL

Diet is often an area which gets neglected in the weeks after the baby is born, simply because we are so busy seeing to the baby's needs, and in all the excitement forget our hunger. But it is a bad policy: nutritious food is energy and energy is something which new mothers need a lot of. Your store of many vital nutrients like iron, folic acid and other vitamins and minerals will also be depleted after the pregnancy and need building up as soon as possible.

If you have postnatal depression, it is even more important to eat a good diet. Increasingly, nutritional research is finding links between a balanced diet and a balanced mind so that it may be that depression itself is triggered by nutritional deficiencies. For example, vitamin B_6

(pyridoxine) is needed to maintain normal mental function, and studies have found that boosting vitamin B_6 in the diet with supplements can lessen the symptoms of depression, particularly depression associated with premenstrual syndrome. Other vitamins and minerals associated with depression when levels run low in the body are folic acid, iron, zinc and selenium as well as certain amino acids needed to produce noradrenaline (norepinephrine) and serotonin.

There may also be a link between blood cholesterol levels and postnatal depression. During pregnancy, levels of cholesterol and triglycerides (fats) rise considerably in the body to take in the extra demands of the baby; they are at their highest just before delivery and then drop rapidly within a few days of the birth. Studies have already established a link between low blood cholesterol levels and mood changes, like aggression, depression and thoughts of suicide; even changing from a medium-fat diet to a low-fat diet can increase feelings of depression and hostility. It is possible, then, that the drop in cholesterol after the birth could trigger postnatal depression or contribute to its development some time after the birth, if cholesterol levels remain low – for example, if the new mother is not eating a nutritious diet.

Caffeine, alcohol and sugar, if consumed in excess, are also associated with an increase in depressive symptoms. Alcohol may seem to give you a lift at the time you drink it but it is actually a depressant, affecting the work of neurotransmitters like serotonin.

A nutritional approach to helping postnatal depression lies in eating a healthy, balanced diet, not going mad cutting out fats and building in plenty of foods which contain the nutrients associated with mood regulation (see Antidepressant Eating, p. 70). Although the fat stores laid down in pregnancy are there to be used up with the birth and while breastfeeding, a nutritious diet is still particularly important: your baby will be taking a lot of calories and nutrients out of you via your milk.

So, aim for a good variety of foods every day, including protein like meat, fish and pulses, carbohydrates like potatoes, bread and rice, dairy or soya products and at least five pieces of fruit and vegetables. You can ensure a spectrum of nutrients from fruit and vegetables by including a range of colours, from oranges and carrots, through green leafy vegetables to red tomatoes and peppers.

If you do not have time or energy to cook, opt for healthier fast-food options and snacks like wholemeal toast/sandwiches, baked potatoes, frozen vegetables pre-prepared fish, tinned fish, tinned tomatoes, yoghurt, fruit and unsweetened breakfast cereals or muesli (a good snack at any time of day!).

Eat little and often to keep your energy levels topped up throughout the day.

When breastfeeding, do not feel you have to eat more than normal but make sure what you do eat is healthy and remember to drink plenty of water, fruit juices etc. to keep up your fluid levels.

Don't go on a low-fat weight loss diet at this stage, as it may make problems with depression worse.

If you are worried that your diet may be lacking in nutrients or that you are nutritionally deficient, take a good multivitamin and mineral supplement to build up your supplies, ensuring it contains those nutrients which are implicated in the development of depression. Plus perhaps, additional vitamin C to help fight off any colds or flu etc your tired body may be vulnerable to. If you feel your depression may be due to a nutritional deficiency and would like to check it out, see a nutritional therapist.

Worries About Weight

Many new mothers worry about their weight: they have put on weight in pregnancy and find that it is still there after the baby is born. This can be discouraging and make

Antidepressant Eating

Deficiencies in some of the following nutrients have been associated with the development of depression; others are likely to be depleted after pregnancy and birth and need boosting in the body. So maximize them in your diet by including as many foods containing these nutrients as possible.

- **Vitamin B$_6$** (pyridoxine)   Fortified breakfast cereals, wholemeal products, nuts, fish, meat (white and red), potatoes, avocado.
- **Folic acid** (folate)   Liver, fortified breakfast cereals, green leafy vegetables.
- **Zinc**   Meat, nuts, wholegrain products (bread, pasta, etc), pulses.
- **Iron**   Fortified breakfast cereals, wholegrain products (bread, pasta, etc), eggs, meat, spinach.
- **Selenium**   Wholemeal products, lentils, bread, seafood, nuts.
- **Calcium**   Dairy products, white bread, fish with bones, (e.g. sardines), green leafy vegetables.
- **Magnesium**   Green leafy vegetables, nuts, wholegrain products
- **Essential fatty acids**   Cod liver oil, oily fish, like mackerel and herring, fresh vegetable oils, nuts.

you feel worse about yourself if you are depressed. However, now is not a good time to think about losing weight. Your priorities are your wellbeing and the baby's. Thinking about dieting, weight loss and so on will be stressful and not in your or the baby's interests. Your nutrient stores may be depleted from the pregnancy and need building up; also, you are in a stressful situation where you need all the energy you can get – and food is energy. If you are depressed, dieting can make you feel worse: you will find it very hard if you are coping with depression to stick to a diet and, if you do not keep to it, it reinforces your view of yourself as a failure.

Bearing this in mind, it is best at this point simply to follow a healthy diet (as outlined above) which will keep your weight steady, and may even help you to lose a few pounds if you are serious about cutting out sugar and very fatty foods. Once the immediate pressures of babycare and postnatal depression are behind you, then you can start dieting if needed. However, remember that it takes time for the body to get back to shape after pregnancy and the weight often shifts of its own accord in the months following the birth; if you are breastfeeding you will probably find that you lose your pregnancy gain quite quickly as breastfeeding helps this process along.

BUILDING EXERCISE INTO YOUR LIFE

If you are dead tired and depressed, exercise can seem like the last thing you want or need. But there are plenty of very good reasons to motivate yourself to get moving, even if it means gritting your teeth and forcing yourself to do it in the initial stages. Build exercise into your life to:

- increase your energy levels and improve your stamina, so that you are more able to meet the physical demands on you;
- help you sleep better if one of the symptoms of your postnatal depression is insomnia;
- help get your body back into shape after the birth;
- make you feel better about yourself and actually lift your depression, because it appears that exercise helps regulate the work of those all-important mood neurotransmitters in the brain. Studies into depression have found that just half an hour of aerobic activity (movement that makes you out of breath) improves mood and anxiety levels for several hours afterwards, and long-term exercise programmes can have a pronounced effect on depression.

However you should not just launch yourself into a fitness programme straight after the birth, as your body will certainly not be ready and you may easily hurt yourself.

First Six Weeks After The Birth

Joints and ligaments are still softened by the body's preparations for the birth at this early stage and so it is easy to cause injury. Start slowly, gently getting your body back into shape by following the postnatal exercise guidelines given by your doctor or postnatal health professional. These are usually aimed at strengthening your pelvic floor (the hoop of muscle with lies under your pelvis supporting the bladder, uterus and bowel), firming up stretched abdominal muscles and improving blood flow to the legs.

Strengthening Your Pelvic Floor

The pelvic floor muscles can become quite stretched after childbirth and will need tightening up again otherwise they may remain slack, leading to problems later with stress incontinence (where urine 'leaks' if you cough, sneeze or jump up and down). This exercise can be done anywhere at any time and is all that is needed to get the pelvic floor back in shape.

Squeeze in your buttocks, drawing in the muscles around your vagina as much as you can and hold for a count of five, then relax. Repeat 10 times, as often as possible during the day.

To remind yourself to do the exercise, put little sticker stars around the house, or learn to associate the exercise with a particular activity, for example, do the exercise while you make tea or coffee, or wait for the lights to change.

If you are not sure where your pelvic floor muscles are, try stopping the flow of urine when you go to the toilet; those muscles which you can feel coming into action are those of your pelvic floor.

From Six Weeks

Now it is safe to increase the amount of exercise you do, but do not jump into anything too strenuous unless you were very fit before and during your pregnancy. Swimming is excellent at this time, as the buoyancy of the water supports the body and takes some of the hard work out of exercising; many sports centres run specially designed postnatal aqua classes which are enormous fun as well as offering a serious workout. If there is no-one to take care of the baby, take him along, too: babies usually take to water like little seals.

Yoga is another gentle introduction to exercise. Look out, too, for postnatal exercise classes which are often run at sports or leisure centres and have crèches attached. If you cannot get out of the house or travel far, then the answer may be a postnatal exercise video, tape or book. These aim to build up the amount and type of exercises you do without straining your body.

Realistically, however, new mothers often find it difficult to fit an exercise class into their routine, and do not find the time or motivation to put on an exercise video on a regular basis; this is particularly true if you are depressed. If you find it difficult to get exercise, the next best thing is to build exercise into your daily life.

- **Keep doing the pelvic floor exercise** outlined (see page 72).
- **Go for walks** with your baby every day, walking briskly. This also gets you out of the house and often lulls the baby to sleep.
- **Run upstairs** for some instant step aerobics.
- **Take the stairs** and not the lift when you are out.
- **Put on music and dance**; you can dance while holding the baby (babies often find this kind of movement comforting).

The point about doing exercise at this time is not that it is going to necessarily get you fit or slimmer but that it will improve your mood, will encourage you to take care of yourself and do things that you find pleasurable. Exercise can also be fun, as long as you find something you enjoy. You do not have to do exercise marathons, either; a little exercise combined with rest and relaxation is a winning combination for anyone who is depressed.

CONTROLLING STRESS

Stress is very much a part of our lives nowadays, but it is important in the postnatal period to take steps to lessen the stress in our lives. The postnatal months are a very demanding time and stress can not only cause depression in the first place but – if the stressful factors continue to exert an influence – consolidate and maintain it.

In order to control stress in our lives, we first have to look at what stresses us the most and what can be changed to alleviate the problem. Chapter 6 has suggestions for lessening stressful babycare problems, but you should also assess your life in its wider context: the amount of work you are trying to cram into a day, your partner's attitude, too many visitors who expect to be waited on, and so on. Then you need to take positive steps to change these stressors.

A lot of stress can come from your relationship with your partner, so it is best to deal with any problems as soon as possible so that they do not start to rankle, promoting tension between you. These issues may range from him not being involved enough or helping out enough with the baby to being too bullying in his advice or expecting too much of you. Whatever the problem, speak to him calmly, explain how you feel and have ready a plan of action on how you can both make positive, simple changes.

Complementary therapies can also help you to tackle stress, whether you use home remedies or see a therapist. Aromatherapy is a particularly good stress-busting therapy, as is massage, meditation and the ancient Chinese exercise system of T'ai chi.

Learning To Relax

Relaxation is another way to alleviate the effects of stress and help to control it but the ability to relax can somehow disappear once there is a baby on the scene. This is where learning specific relaxation techniques can help. These techniques are not just a matter of lying down with one's eyes closed. They are an easily learnt and well-tested means of letting go of stress and anxiety, combining muscle relaxation with focused mental relaxation. Start by losing tension from your body before moving on to lowering levels of mental stress through visualization. All it takes is a commitment to put aside 10 to 20 minutes a day, every day.

In Your Relaxation Programme (p. 76), you will find a basic guide to relaxation techniques. If you prefer, though, there is usually a good selection of relaxation tapes available from bookshops and health stores which can guide you through a prerecorded routine; these usually include a muscle relaxation programme and a mental visualization exercise accompanied by calming music or sounds. Although they are based on hypnotherapy techniques, there is no worry about losing control or 'going under'. The process is very gentle, works around you allowing yourself to let go, and is completely safe for most people (consult your doctor before using a relaxation tape, however, if you suffer from epilepsy).

A visualization exercise is simply a calming scenario to help you relax. It can either be a generalized calming scene, for example, lying on a tropical beach listening to the waves; lying on warm grass beside a stream with the sun touching your face; walking through a wood along a winding path, the scent of pine around you; listening to the birds, lying watching the clouds. Or, alternatively, you can call up somewhere peaceful you have been to in life, somewhere you were calm and happy, and hold that scene in your mind. With depression, you can visualize images aimed at lessening feelings of despondency and entrapment. For example, you might imagine yourself in a dark room with the sun slowly rising outside and sending streams of light into the room. Or you could visualize yourself at the bottom of a dark hole, slowly climbing a ladder to the light at the top. As you go through the visualization, don't worry if thoughts intrude: just let them skate across your mind and then let go of them.

If you are a beginner at this type of relaxation process, find a quiet room in the house where you can lie down and not be disturbed; make sure it is warm and you are wearing loose comfortable clothing. Once you become used to it, however, you should be able to go through the process anywhere for instant stress release when it is needed. For example, if the baby is having a bad day and is crying for

---

Your Relaxation Programme

1 Lie down somewhere comfortable and close your eyes. Focus on your breathing: breathe in through the nose and take the breath down into your stomach. Feel your stomach rise as you inhale and fall as you exhale. Breathe slowly and regularly.

2 Starting at your feet, tense or squeeze your foot muscles for five seconds and then let go and relax them for 10–15 seconds. Slowly move up your body (legs, stomach, back, shoulders/neck, arms and face), tensing/squeezing the muscles in each area for five seconds, then relaxing them for around 10 seconds before moving on.

3 Tense your whole body, hold for five seconds then let it all go.

4 Go through your body, checking for any remaining areas of tension, and follow the tense–relax programme again if you find any.

5 Visualize yourself somewhere peaceful and happy and allow your mind to relax. Do not chase any thoughts that enter your mind; let them go and continue with your visualization.

6 When you feel ready and totally relaxed, re-focus on your breathing and open your eyes. Get up slowly and give your body a good stretch to end the relaxation exercise.

long periods, go out of earshot and run through your relaxation programme, which will recharge you, give you a reviving rest and help you to cope with the crying.

Good Breathing Practice

Breathing is also a part of the relaxation process and breathing is often affected when we are under stress or overanxious. In such emotional situations, we tend to breathe quickly and shallowly and a prolonged episode of this type of breathing leads to hyperventilation, where the balance of oxygen and carbon dioxide in the body is upset, causing a range of symptoms, such as breathing difficulties, tight chest or chest pains, trembling, tingling, dizziness and lethargy. It can make the person feel panicky and out of control, which will exacerbate the other symptoms of postnatal depression and stop coping mechanisms from springing into action.

If you find that you tend to overbreathe under stress, consciously slow down your breathing with the following exercise.

1 Exhale as much stale air from your lungs as possible by giving a long sighing out-breath.
2 With one hand on your stomach, breathe in through your nose and let the breath go down to your stomach. You should feel your stomach rise.
3 Hold for a few seconds and let the breath go slowly out through your nose. One breathing cycle should take around eight seconds. If an eight-second cycle feels uncomfortable, start with a five-second cycle and build up to eight seconds as you practise.

Good Posture

Posture is important in the postnatal period, particularly as holding yourself properly now can help prevent back problems developing later. But in addition to this, the way we hold ourselves will mirror our mood and also give a good indication of whether we are feeling depressed, stressed or anxious (hunched shoulders, head down, stiff neck, clenched jaw . . .). Simply by relaxing and improving posture, we can help alleviate these feelings. If you would like to take posture a step further, then learning a posturally based health programme, like the Alexander technique, Pilates or yoga, can help make good posture a way of life. A relaxation session at least once a day is another way to make you more aware of tension in your body.

Certainly, the least you should do when you are under pressure or feeling overanxious is check your posture through the day and consciously relax tensed areas. Betty Parsons, a well-known British childbirth educator who has seen royal babies into the world, maintains that the best advice she has ever given new mothers is simply, 'Shoulders down!' She has found that just by reminding yourself throughout the day to drop hunched, tense shoulders, you can lessen your own tension, stress and feelings of frustration.

TIME FOR YOURSELF

Tender loving care is often in short supply for new mothers, when the focus is firmly fixed on the baby, and the new mother is often the last on her own list for rest, relaxation and recuperation. But this should not be the case. Being mother to a new baby is a 24-hour job and, without let-up, it can grind you down, leaving you less able to cope when the baby is demanding or tetchy. Every mother needs to build a relaxing time into her day – 'Me Time', if you like – so that she can recharge her batteries and find space in her life for herself.

Me Time is good policy for any mother, but it is doubly so for a mother suffering from postnatal depression, where depression, frustration and feelings of anger find little outlet, building up until there is an explosion. Scheduling time in every day to do something that you enjoy can act as a safety valve as well as helping you to hold onto the 'me' in you that is sometimes swallowed up by being a mother.

Me Time is basically time put aside each day to do something that you enjoy, which relaxes you and makes you happy. It does not have to be a long time; 10 minutes when the baby is sleeping can be enough to recharge the batteries. What you have to remember to do is schedule it; Me Time is easily lost among all the other calls on your attention which can seem more important. They are not. For your sanity's sake, Me Time in a day should take priority; leave the housework.

It is best not to schedule this time too definitely, as it leads to frustration if something occurs which stops you from taking your time out. Just make a decision that, every day, at some point, you are going to take some time and dedicate it to yourself. What you spend the time doing depends on you and what you enjoy. Lying down listening to music, knitting, solving crosswords, reading, doing an exercise video, gardening, painting your nails, styling your hair, fussing the cat, or simply doing nothing, just relaxing . . .

It can help to have a special place – a sanctuary – that you can go for Me Time. It does not have to be a particular room – just a corner of a room will do. Place a comfortable armchair in your nook and fill it with your treasures – photos, favourite ornaments, toys, books, music, a pot of flowers, a bowl of fruit – and try to decorate the corner in your favourite colours. Adding an essential oil burner and perhaps some candles can also help you to relax and feel that you are taking part in 'special time'. Choose essential oils which help with depression like, clary sage, melissa, rose and ylang ylang, or those which are good for stress such as bergamot, lavender, neroli and jasmine.

This nook can become your haven, which you can retreat to when everything becomes too much and you need a break. The rest of the family should know that your time there is sacrosanct and you are not to be disturbed. It might even be helpful to tell your partner that, if the baby starts crying while you are having Me Time, you would be grateful if he could see to him. When you are on your own with the baby, make sure Me Time starts as soon as baby falls asleep so you are assured of at least 10 minutes' worth of relaxation and recooperation, even if your baby is a short napper.

Although it may be difficult at first to motivate yourself to take the self-help steps outlined here, it is undoubtedly worth the initial effort. They can help you to feel more in control of your life while arming you to fight the depression and giving you the buzz of knowing that, depression apart, you are capable of doing something positive – and that is half the battle won.

CHAPTER 6

Tackling Babycare Problems

Looking after a newborn baby involves broken nights, long days, snatched sleep, tension, juggling meals and housework, tiredness, endless visitors and perhaps feeding problems, too.

> 'You get a lot of attention in pregnancy. But once the baby's here, that's it. Now the baby gets all the attention. I'm working harder than I ever have and not getting much credit for it. No wonder I feel down.' Jane, mother to a 18-month-old Holly.

> 'I had never imagined the terrible tiredness. It dragged me right down and turned everything grey and dingy. I longed for Graham to sleep through the night but I don't think I got a decent night's sleep until he was about six months old.' Georgina, mother to 18-month-old Graham.

When I became pregnant with my second baby, it was not the thought of the birth that bothered me, but the knowledge that I would have to get through the first three months again! Little surprise, then, to find that this is the peak time for depression to develop, as mothers battle with babycare problems as well as coming to terms with all the emotional upheavals.

If you suffer from postnatal depression, getting your basic babycare routine running smoothly will help take the pressure off in many ways, and there are three babycare hotspots that come up again and again as high-stress areas for parents: breastfeeding, sleep and crying. Here, I target those areas and offer some self-help suggestions to lower the amount of stress they cause, keep a sense of perspective, give you a plan of action and help you feel more in control.

PROBLEMS WITH BREASTFEEDING

Once upon a time, when breastfeeding was the only safe option for feeding an infant, girls grew up seeing other women breastfeed their babies and when their turn came, they already knew how to do it. They were also surrounded by other mothers who had already breastfed and could offer advice if it was needed.

Then 'progress' moved in on the scene and formula milk was invented. With the advent of formula milk, the old pattern changed, particularly with the generation who are now starting their own families, as many of our own mothers may not have breastfed any of their babies. We grew up watching babies being bottle-fed.

Now, however, as we discover the enormous benefits breastfeeding offers children, more new mothers prefer to breastfeed their babies. However, that vital breastfeeding link that mothers in the past enjoyed may not be around, so many new breastfeeding mothers feel unconfident.

We also tend to invest a lot of our belief in ourselves as mothers in our ability to breastfeed our baby. In some ways, this is a result of breastfeeding being more actively promoted by health professionals. Because the number of mothers breastfeeding beyond six weeks is low, governments, health professionals and other interested organizations have – quite rightly – been active in pointing out the advantages breastfeeding offers over bottle feeding with formula milk. But in many cases, although the message is getting across to mothers, the support and expert advice which should go hand in hand with the message is lagging behind. This means many mothers experiencing breast-feeding problems may have no-one to turn to, receive conflicting advice from a succession of professionals (including the doctor) and then feel a failure when they turn to formula in despair. If you are depressed already, then this feeling may filter into other areas of caring for your baby so that you come to doubt your abilities as a mother generally.

> *'With my first baby, I had very sore, cracked nipples,'* says Elaine *'The pain was excruciating for about the first minute of Danny sucking and then it all went numb – until the next time. One midwife I saw recommended a nipple shield. The next day a different midwife more or less whipped the shield off my breast with the words "We don't use those anymore." Confused? You bet I was. And still sore and very despondent about the whole feeding thing.'* Elaine ended up bottle feeding Danny after two weeks of trying to breastfeed and dreading every minute of it. *'It started to affect everything to do with him. I was very unhappy and, in the end, felt it just wasn't worth it.'*

We know that breastfeeding difficulties are greatest in the first two to three weeks after the birth: for example, around 20 per cent of UK mothers who opt to breastfeed give up within this time. The main problem areas tend to be:

- getting the baby positioned correctly on the breast (the so-called 'latched-on' position)
- sore and cracked nipples which make breastfeeding painful
- baby wants to feed at the breast constantly, or you cannot seem to produce enough milk to satisfy her.

Many women believe that they are not producing enough milk for their baby because she seems continually hungry and demanding, but the problem is more likely to be the fact that she is not positioned in such a way as to be able to draw milk from the breast efficiently. Your breasts produce

Bonuses Of Breastfeeding

If breastfeeding has hit problems and you need a little extra encouragement, keep in mind all the reasons why it is good for you and the baby. Breastmilk:

- is always available, always the right temperature, and doesn't need any special equipment;
- follows a simple supply-and-demand rule: the more the baby sucks, the more milk the mother makes;
- contains the perfect balance of proteins, fats and watery fluids so that your baby has food and drink in one go;
- contains all the valuable antibodies – and more – which protect the baby from life threatening infections and help build her immune system. A baby's immune system remains immature until about 12 months;
- decreases the chances of the baby developing allergy-related illnesses like eczema, asthma and coeliac disease (allergy to gluten).

Breastfeeding:

- may help to calm your baby. Research suggests that the act of suckling releases calming hormones in the baby; the hormones you produce while breastfeeding also calm you down. Because the milk is always available baby can be fed at any time (no need to time feeds or clock watch) so does not became fretful while bottles are being prepared;
- can help your body get back into shape after the birth. Breastfeeding encourages your womb to contract back after the birth and it can help get rid of weight in areas where fat deposits are usually hard to shift, like around your thighs and buttocks;
- once it is going well, it can strengthen the mother/baby relationship, creating a close bond. It can also help you build up your confidence in yourself and your abilities.

milk in response to demand from the baby and if that demand is not forthcoming, then they will not produce the milk and so it may seem that you are not able to satisfy your baby.

Positioning is the key to successful breastfeeding and most breastfeeding problems – like cracked nipples – come down to the baby not being properly latched on. Of course, it is easy to say 'get the positioning right' but actually achieving it can be hard while your baby and you are learning the ropes. Breastfeeding books and leaflets can give you step-by-step guides but new mothers really need to be *shown how* to do it by someone who is experienced in breastfeeding, whose advice is consistent and who can be there until the mother becomes practised in the technique.

If you are experiencing breastfeeding difficulties and they are making you feel depressed or interfering with your developing relationship with your baby, it is important to find consistent, sympathetic help. Contacting a breastfeeding support organization (eg La Leche League) will provide the support and consistent expert advice you may be needing. But other mothers may be able to help you, too, whether it is someone in the family, a friend, or via a postnatal support group. Increasingly, babycare organizations and charities are training mothers to be breastfeeding counsellors, so that they can help others to breastfeed successfully. There are a number of organizations involved in this, the most well known internationally being La Leche League, which has branches in most countries.

It is really worth contacting a breastfeeding organization or counsellor if you are having problems, and to do so quickly. When breastfeeding is going well, you feel contented, happy, and at times blissful; if it is not going well, it can leave you feeling frustrated, angry at yourself and the baby, guilty and depressed.

If you are having problems, it may also help to remember the following. You are not alone. Many mothers experience some problems and soreness in the first few weeks, even those who are breastfeeding for the second or third time. Keep a sense of perspective and try not to let it dominate your early life with the baby. The most difficult time usually only lasts a few weeks, by which time both you and the baby will have learnt how to breastfeed. If your nipples become too cracked and painful to feed, it is possible for you to stop until they heal and then go back to breastfeeding. In the meantime, gently express milk for a few days: your breasts will start reproducing milk once the baby stimulates the milk flow again. If you decide to do this, however, talk to your health professional or breastfeeding counsellor first, so they can guide you through.

You still have the option of bottle feeding if you really feel you cannot cope with breastfeeding and it is driving a wedge between you and the baby. And if you make this decision, you are not a failure nor a bad mother: you are still doing the best for your baby because best for baby is to be close to her mother – not having a mother who feels angry, frustrated, guilty or depressed.

SLEEPING DIFFICULTIES

Ask most new parents, and they will agree that tiredness is the hardest part of having a new baby. Newborn babies sleep on average around 16 hours a day; unfortunately this is usually in stretches of only a few hours' at a time, and that includes during the night. So, in the early days, a mother will probably not enjoy a long stretch of uninterrupted sleep at night, but will be woken two or three times and then find herself up at the crack of dawn in the morning.

Many babies settle into a routine after the first two to three months, starting to have a longer period of sleep during the night. However, this is by no means the case with all babies. Many continue to wake for night feeds or comfort right through the first year: one study found that around 40 per cent of nine-month-olds had not yet slept through the night. As one father says:

'It wasn't the waking in the first few months that was the problem – we were expecting that. It was the fact that it didn't let up and we still weren't getting a decent night's sleep six months later.'

Lack of rest can cause you to become depressed, as well as making depression worse. Again, it develops into a vicious circle: exhaustion triggers or exacerbates depression, which can in itself cause sleep problems, which in turn makes the new mother even more fatigued. In the end, it is difficult to know what emotions are due to extreme tiredness and what are caused by depression – one reason why it is often hard for doctors to diagnose postnatal depression.

If you have a baby who, after the first few months, still has a broken sleeping routine, there are steps you can take to help both yourself fight tiredness and your baby to become a better night-time sleeper.

- Take care of your health, eat well and take some exercise outside.
- Join your baby when she naps during the day. There is always the temptation to catch up on chores when the baby is asleep, but if you are suffering from extreme fatigue, it is a far better policy to rest up during this time. If you find it difficult to sleep, then simply do something restful: put your feet up, read a book or magazine, watch something undemanding on the TV, paint your nails, have a foot bath – anything which demands little effort but which you find relaxing and enjoyable.
- Learn to relax. Doing a 15-minute relaxation routine while the baby naps can refresh you, even if you do not actually sleep. You will find more on relaxation techniques in Chapter 5.
- Ask someone to get up for the baby in your place. If your partner usually shares the night-time waking, he may not be the best person to ask, as he too will be tired. If possible, ask your mother or mother-in-law, a close friend or other family member to stay the night and step in to give you both a rest.
- It may be that your baby has got into 'unsociable' sleeping habits, so you can try taking steps to get her into a sleeping routine (see p. 88).

If things are really bad and your baby's sleeping problems are contributing to your depression, seek outside help. Your doctor or health professional will have advice tailored to your situation and your local health centre may even run a sleep clinic to which your doctor will be able to refer you. Although by no means widespread, these clinics are becoming increasingly common and are very successful in helping parents who are experiencing sleep difficulties with their child.

Establishing A Sleep Routine

Babies need a routine of some sort; in fact, they find routine comforting in many ways – they are more settled if they know what to expect, when. Sleep is no exception, so it is important to establish a bedtime routine as soon as possible.

- Keep to a strict time for both going to bed and taking naps during the day.
- Make sure that the run-up to bedtime is a wind-down with no active rough and tumble play. Try reading books, singing rhymes or just talking to your baby instead. It may be better for wind-down to take place in the bedroom, as elsewhere often offers too many other distractions.
- Have a set pattern of bedtime activities, ie bath, feed, wind-down play, then bed.
- Try to put the baby to bed awake, rather than letting her fall asleep while having a last feed or being rocked in your arms. Eventually, baby has to learn to get herself asleep, in which case this may help.
- Have a regular bedtime rhyme or phrase, even if it is only, 'Goodnight, sleep tight', to let her know that now it is time to go to sleep. If possible, do not stay in the room while she falls asleep.

- Try to avoid bringing her back downstairs again after you have put her to bed. This only gives the message that bedtime is flexible as long as she screams and cries loud enough. It is better for you to go up to her and stay a while.
- If she does wake in the night, be as boring as possible. Do not chat or sing or play games; keep talking to a minimum while reassuring your baby. In older babies, past the night-feed stage, do not offer a bottle of milk (a nice reward for waking); offer water instead. Invest in a night light to keep the lights dim or turn on a light in another room. Your basic message to your baby is that night is for sleeping not playing.

If sleeping problems persist, there are a number of avenues you can try. On the one hand, you may find you get a better night's sleep if your baby comes into bed with you. This approach works for many parents: breastfeeding is simple (you do not even have to get out of bed), baby is secure because you are always near, and because she sleeps better, you do too. However, many babies do not like to move back into their cot and this in itself can become a problem at a later date when your small, still infant has turned into a bigger, wigglier one-year-old. It is true, too, that many babies do not like being in with Mum and Dad, possibly because they get overheated.

At the other extreme is the 'controlled crying' approach to establishing a bedtime routine. This basically means putting your baby to bed and letting her cry herself to sleep with you going in at regular intervals to reassure her. The step-by-step plan is:

- Get a relaxing bedtime routine in place (see above), then put her in her cot, say goodnight and leave the room. Be decisive and show her that you mean business.
- If she cries, go back, reassure her briefly and then leave again. If the cries start up again, wait two minutes then repeat the reassurance process, picking her up only if

necessary to calm her and only briefly before putting her in her cot again.

- Build up your waiting time to 20 minutes before going and checking on her and continue at 20-minute intervals until she falls asleep. It could take some time, but be persistent and determined.
- Follow this procedure if she wakes in the night.

According to advocates of this approach, it can mean two or three nights of very broken sleep with a lot of crying (probably from both baby and parents) but finally the baby will get the message that night is for sleeping. It is not an easy strategy for parents to follow, however, and it does not work for all babies: after all, a baby cries because she wants you; if you don't come – or come and go baby may learn you are not reliable and this may in turn increase her anxiety and stress. So, if after four nights of crying there is little sign of improvement, seek the advice of your doctor or health professional.

Whatever approach you decide on really depends on you, your baby and your situation. Many parents do not like the idea of bed sharing; others find the controlled crying approach too soul destroying to contemplate. But where lack of sleep is causing major problems in a family, including depression, then it is vital that you take some action.

THE CRYING BABY

Having a baby who cries a lot can trigger or exacerbate depression as well as causing parents – especially the mother – frustration, worry, guilt and despair.

First of all, it is worth remembering that all babies cry, it is just a matter of degree. Crying in the early weeks, before your baby has even learnt to smile, is her only means of communication. It can say 'I am hungry', 'I am wet or dirty', 'I am hot', 'I am cold', 'I have wind', 'I have a pain' or, quite simply, 'I need you'.

Babies also commonly have a 'crying time' when their crying takes on a new intensity. Often called three-month colic, because it occurs in the first three to four months after the birth, it can seem as though the baby is in pain, drawing her legs up to her stomach. This crying time usually occurs at the same time each day, often in the early evening (and lasting sometimes until 10 or 11 o'clock at night) just the time, significantly, when parents themselves are feeling most ragged. During this time, the baby will cry inconsolably. Parents may try everything – feeding, changing, holding, comforting and so on – to no avail.

'Three-month colic' is difficult to deal with, particularly since there is always the worry that the baby is actually ill and not just crying. But it does appear to be a normal part of development. Why it occurs we are not sure: it could be wind, tiredness or, more likely, a response to all the stimuli of the day on the baby's developing senses. But in time you will know when your baby's crying time is and learn to interpret her crying so that you can pick up when something is not right. As always, if you are at all worried, call a doctor.

After a while, most mothers become adept at interpreting their baby's cry and knowing what she is saying. This does not happen right at the start, when mother and baby are just getting to know each other; and sometimes, it does not click in until later, depending on the mother and the baby. If a mother has depression, for example, then communication may be disturbed and the mother may not be able to understand what the baby wants, and this will lead to a more difficult, crying baby and a more depressed mother. This is why it is so important for mothers to seek help for early-occurring depression, so that the problem can be nipped in the bud before communication problems between mother and baby become disrupted and make the situation worse.

Comforting Tactics

If your baby is crying, first run through a crying checklist to ensure none of the following is causing the problem.

- Is anything hurting her, such as a bit of wool caught around a finger, nappy digging in, uncomfortable clothing, and so on?
- Is she hungry or thirsty?
- Is her nappy clean?
- Does she have wind?
- Is she too hot or too cool?
- Is she bored?
- Is she teething?
- Does she need a cuddle?
- Is she overstimulated and needing a quiet time to recover?
- Is she sick/does she have a temperature?

If none of these appears to be the problem, there are other tactics you can try to comfort and calm a crying baby.

- Movement can often work, so walk her up and down, holding her. Find out what type of movement comforts her best; some babies like rocking, others like gentle jiggling.
- Get a sling or baby pouch and carry her around with you, whatever you're doing. She may well like the security of being held close to you.
- Give her a bath.
- Put the baby in her pushchair and go for a walk. The movement and change in air often helps.
- Get in the car and go for a ride. Again, the car movement seems to lull babies to sleep.
- Put her near the washing machine or dishwasher if it is on. The noise can comfort babies.
- Place her facing a window, where she can see branches or clouds moving; in summer, open the window and let the breeze move the curtains. In warmer weather you could put her in her pram/pushchair in the garden, too, only place her somewhere where you can watch her.
- Try a dummy for a short time, but wean her off it after the first few months so that it does not become a permanent accessory.

Reaching Breaking Point

Crying can truly drive you to the end of your tether, if it is unrelenting and there is little you can do to comfort your baby. In this situation, you may find that you are close to hurting your baby and it is then vital to put space between you. If possible, call someone around to take over for a few hours while you get out of the house. If this is not possible, then place your baby somewhere where she cannot come to harm (in her crib or cot) and then leave the room, go out of earshot and calm down. You can do this by putting into action the relaxation techniques outlined in Chapter 5 (see p. 76) or you can take out all your frustration on an inanimate object like a cushion or mattress. Scream if you feel the need to. Then, when you are calmer, go back to your baby.

There are also organizations you can get in touch with for support and advice on coping with a crying baby and these will give advice on depression, too, as the two often go hand in hand. Most operate helplines for times of crisis which are usually manned by parents who have had a crying baby, so they will understand what you are going through. These organizations are listed in Useful Addresses (see p. 116).

ASK FOR SUPPORT

These first months with the baby are probably among the most stressful you will ever experience, so accept help where it is offered, as long as you know the person and the offer is genuine, and not an excuse to come around to chat, drink coffee and leave a pile of washing-up behind! If you need help and know someone who would be willing to step in, then do not be shy about asking. Probably the only reason she (or he) has not already offered is that you have given the impression you are coping fine and do not need help.

Be specific about what kind of help you would like. Ideas include cooking or bringing round a meal; doing some cleaning or housework; babysitting while you take a bath or shower, go shopping, or simply rest; grocery shopping for you; or driving you and the baby to the doctor or clinic, avoiding the inconvenience of waiting for a bus.

Beyond the practical things, other people can also step in as emotional supporters. If you have friends with babies, then get in contact with them or re-establish links if you have let them lapse during the pregnancy or due to your depression.

If you don't know anyone in your area, then find out if there is a local mothers' group in action. There is a range of support groups around, some which provide a general meeting point for mothers with babies and young children, and others which offer specialist help, for example for breastfeeding mothers, working mothers, or those suffering from postnatal depression:

> *'It was such a relief to meet up with someone who felt the same as I did,'* said Felicity, who started going to a local postnatal support group recommended by her health professional. *'One mum had a baby who was about six months older than Libby but I can't tell you how good it was when she described her depression and her feelings were so similar to what I was experiencing.'*

To find out if there are any groups in your area, look on the noticeboard at your clinic, ask your doctor or health professional or contact one of the organizations listed under Useful Addresses (see p. 116).

Try not to be too shy or depressed to make the effort to join a mother's group. It can seem daunting to walk into a room of strangers but keep in mind that these mothers did not know each other before joining the group, and that you all have one thing in common: your babies. The other mothers are there because they, too, want and need support and a chance to chat about worries with other mothers. Finding out that other mothers are feeling the same and having similar problems – be they emotional or practical – can make worries smaller. You never know, you may even find yourself laughing about them.

'The first time I laughed in around a month was talking to other mums about the trials of breastfeeding,' Georgina remembers. *'We'd all had similar experiences and suddenly all the soreness, the leakiness, the hours spend wondering if the baby was feeding or actually asleep, were put in perspective for me and didn't seem half so bad.'*

CHAPTER 7

Postnatal Depression and Special Babies

If depression can be a problem for a mother with one healthy baby, then it is logical to assume it will be more of a problem for mothers of multiples, or those with a baby who is ill or disabled. Studies back up this supposition: mothers of twins, for example, have around double the chance of developing postnatal depression in the first six months after delivery, compared with mothers of single babies.

For families coping with twins or more, or with a baby who is ill or disabled, the normal pressures of early parenthood are intensified. They have less time for themselves and any other children in the family, and the mother may be more isolated, for the simple reason that she is less able to get out of the house than other mothers.

MORE THAN ONE BABY

The pressures of having more than one newborn start at the birth. Mothers of multiples are far more likely to have an assisted delivery; for example, an enormous 65 per cent of triplet births in the UK are by Caesarean section. As already mentioned in Chapter 2, assisted deliveries, and particularly Caesarean sections, are a risk factor for post-natal depression. A multiple birth is also more likely to produce premature and low birthweight babies, so right from the start they may require special care. These babies are at higher risk of health problems or disability; the incidence of cerebral palsy, for example, increases five-fold in multiples. Sick newborns may spend their first few weeks in the neonatal special care unit and twins may not even be cared for in the same hospital, if one baby has to go into a specialist unit. This means parents have to divide their time between one hospital and another.

Sadly, multiple births also increase the risk of perinatal death and parents may find themselves in the agonizing position of mourning one baby while trying to take care of and establish a relationship with the surviving newborn. In effect, they are celebrating and grieving at the same time.

Once discharged from hospital, parents of twins and multiples generally get very little additional support, even though the sheer practicalities of taking care of more than one newborn are immense. Feeding takes longer to master and get established: breastfeeding two or even three babies is a difficult craft to learn and very often new mothers are not given much guidance on how to breastfeed multiples successfully. Problems with crying are intensified, as the babies may set each other off, or develop the same 'crying time', so you are trying to calm two or more simultaneously. As one mother of triplets puts it: 'I only have two arms. If I pick them up, I always have to make a decision about which one I am going to leave behind'.

As already mentioned, lack of support is one of the most significant triggers in the development of postnatal depression. Mothers of multiples can find themselves very isolated, because it is more difficult for them to get out of the house (shopping with triplets is a logistic nightmare), they are probably on a tight budget and have more physical babycare to get through than other mothers. A knock-on effect of this is that they miss out on morale boosting from other parents or feedback on babycare worries.

It can be difficult for other family members to help out, too. Grandparents – often the mainstay of new mothers – may be willing to help out but not able to: looking after one newborn is taxing enough for an older person, but two or three? In addition, people looking in from the outside are not always aware of how much extra work and emotional pressure having more than one baby is.

Mothers of multiples also get no time alone and can begin to feel subsumed by being a mother. Emotionally, it can be exhausting sharing your love between two or more newborns, all crying for attention. Getting good communication going between mother and baby will be more difficult, and depression adds to communication difficulties.

The key to overcoming depression if you are a mother of twins or more babies is support, support, support. Any mother in this situation should be doggedly persistent in seeking that support, from whatever quarter she can.

If you are depressed, see your doctor or talk to your health professional. You will then receive prompt treatment and it may also open up the possibility of practical help in the form of a nurse helper or childcare trainee visiting on a regular basis.

Find out what practical help is available to mothers of multiples, for example home help, babysitting, assistance for low-income families and other financial benefits. Approach involved charities and voluntary organizations, who may be able to offer assistance. Unfortunately, there is not usually much official help for parents of multiples and, where you are entitled to something, you often have to be persistent about getting it. Off your own back, you could try approaching local training colleges to see if they have any nurse or childcare trainees who would be interested in work experience looking after twins or more.

Do not try to hide your problems from family and friends who might be able to help you. If they ask to help, tell them exactly what you would like them to do. Even if practical babycare – feeding, changing, and so on – is beyond them, there are still plenty of other jobs around which eat into your time but which they could quite easily cover: washing up, putting the washing in the machine, vacuuming, buying groceries, bringing in or preparing a hot meal, and so on.

Find other mothers in your situation so you have someone with whom you can share your particular problems and worries. Twins and multiple birth organizations run twins' clubs in most areas, some with specialist meetings for parents with disabled twins, or following fertility treatment, or after a bereavement. As well as providing support, they often also organize parties and social events, a babysitting rota and clothing and equipment sales.

Having more than one newborn is hard work, but most mothers of twins or more admit that it gets easier as the children get older and the sheer physical exertion and exhaustion of having newborns gives way to toddlers who are more able to entertain and help themselves. One advantage of having more than one is that they always have ready-made playmates, even if they do argue more than they agree!

DEPRESSION AFTER ASSISTED CONCEPTION

It can be hard to understand why women who desperately wanted a baby should succumb to postnatal depression when their wish becomes reality. It may be that fertility treatment itself causes more hormonal upheaval than normally occurs in a pregnancy. Certainly, there is some research to suggest that severe depression in the week after the birth is more prevalent in women who have undergone fertility treatment to conceive. But there are other social and emotional reasons why postnatal depression appears a risk for mothers after fertility treatment.

First, if a couple has been having treatment for infertility for some time, it may become difficult for them to see beyond getting pregnant. It then comes as a shock when the baby actually arrives and life as a family begins. It may only be now that the responsibility of having and caring for a baby dawn on the new parents, bringing with it feelings of anxiety and panic which may lead to depression when coupled with fatigue and stress.

Second, mothers who conceive after fertility treatment may have higher expectations of both motherhood and themselves than those who conceive straightforwardly. The feeling is 'I've waited so long for this baby, I am going to love him and take such good care of him. Everything is going to be perfect.' But reality is not like this and it can be difficult for new mothers in this situation to reconcile the image they had of themselves with the tired, crotchety, short-tempered and frustrated person early motherhood has made them.

Those closest to the mother may also have high expectations of her, because she wanted a baby so badly. So they may not offer as much help as they would normally, feeling she would rather take care of the baby herself. Having high expectations and little support is a double blow for new mothers as they come down to earth with a bump.

It is also more likely that women who have had an assisted conception will have an assisted delivery, possibly because both doctors and parents are concerned that, having come this far, there should be no last-minute problems. Again, not being able to deliver your long-awaited baby yourself may dent your high expectations and leave you feeling less in control.

Control is an interesting aspect of assisted conception and one which may have some bearing on postnatal depression. Many women who conceive spontaneously talk about feeling 'out of control' during the birth if proceedings are taken out of their hands by the medical team. In turn, this handing-over of control is thought to be involved in creating a cycle of misgiving and anxiety in new mothers, which may increase the likelihood of depression. Yet in assisted conception, control is handed over to the doctors from the start: they have control over conception, let alone the pregnancy and birth. But once the birth is over and mother and baby go home, control is suddenly, completely, given back to the mother.

> '*I felt like I was dropped, really,*' said one mum who had *in vitro* fertilization (IVF) treatment and conceived after three years of trying. '*After all the attention, I was out on my own, and to be honest, I didn't have a clue. I thought I would be a wonderful mother naturally even if I couldn't conceive naturally. But I wasn't.*'

Most of the steps outlined in Chapters 5 and 6 will be relevant to mothers suffering from depression after an assisted conception, but additionally there are organizations specializing in fertility problems which also offer postnatal advice for people adjusting to becoming parents. You will find these listed in Useful Addresses (see p. 116). They may be able to put you in touch with other parents in your area who have had an assisted conception. The hospital which treated you may also have a contact register of other, similar parents.

Meeting other mothers generally – through local support groups or clubs – can also help you to adjust to the normality of your situation and get your expectations of motherhood into perspective. You will at the very least learn how other mothers – regardless of how much they wanted and love their baby – also lose their temper, feel frustrated, can't keep the house clean and endure night after night of broken sleep!

IF YOUR BABY IS ILL OR DISABLED

Advances in technology and modern obstetrics have made us come to expect the delivery of a healthy newborn baby every time. Sadly, this is not the case. There are many babies who are born ill or who have some kind of physical or mental disability. Because we have high expectations of everything being fine, it can come as an undeniable shock to parents if their baby has a problem and it can certainly make establishing a close relationship with the baby more difficult, at least in the early days.

Caring for a baby in these situations is also more fraught and parents will go through far greater emotional seesaw-ing (feeling anxiety, hope, disappointment) and, very often, guilt, too, that it was something they did which caused the problem. Mothers in these situations have a greater chance of developing depression.

Special Care Babies

There are a number of reasons why a newborn might need to spend time in a special care unit, and not all of them are serious. Premature or low birthweight babies will often need some time in special care; other reasons include jaun-dice, physical problems like cleft palate or clicky hip, and more serious complications like babies born needing surgery or those who have a disability.

Having a baby in special care can be a bewildering and distressing experience for parents. It is easy to feel that care of the new baby has been handed over to the paediatric nurses and doctors. Very often, the mother will be placed in a hospital ward along with mothers with healthy babies, which places an extra emotional burden on her as she watches other mothers caring and holding their healthy babies.

The special care unit itself can be daunting to parents, however determined they are to be with their baby. All the monitors, wires and equipment can make parents afraid to touch their baby in case they dislodge something or hurt him. Parents may also feel despondent and guilty that their new baby has had this traumatic experience so early in his life; some feel it is in some way their fault, even though there is no blame in these situations.

If your baby remains in special care after you have been discharged, visiting may be difficult, particularly if he is in a specialist unit some distance from home, or if you have other children to take care of. There is also the ever-present worry about the baby's condition, and the incessant prayer that all will be well.

These are pressures of a very particular kind and it is easy to become depressed, either as it is all happening or as a delayed reaction once the immediate pressure is off. All your expectations about starting life with your baby have had to be put on hold and it can seem as though you are in limbo, with strangers taking over the caring that should be yours.

If you are in this situation, take steps to alleviate the emotional pressures. Visit your baby as often as you can and hold him whenever possible so that he knows your touch, the sound of your voice and your smell. A baby very quickly responds to his mother, because he already knows you from the nine months spent inside! He will soon recognize and prefer you to the other caregivers around him.

Try to give him your breastmilk as this will give a vulnerable baby the best protection against infection. It will probably mean expressing milk until he is able to feed from the breast. Nursing staff will be able to help you to express your milk and will be keen to help you feed your baby in this way.

Talk to your partner about how you are feeling and encourage him to talk to you, so that you build up an emotional two-way communication which will prepare you for when the baby comes home.

Try not to hide your emotions, find someone you feel you can talk to. This may be your partner, but if you feel you cannot be that open with him because it would add to his distress, then look for someone else who empathizes with you and will be a good listener.

Don't worry if you do not feel particularly close to your baby at this time. Special care can distance parents from their baby. When your baby does come home, follow hospital advice of course, but also work towards being ordinary parents and get away from thinking your baby is different. You are normal parents with a normal baby – you have just had a start to family life which is little different from other parents'. And the baby will be ready to bond with you.

If you find that you are becoming increasingly depressed and unable to cope with the pressure of having a sick baby, then seek help. In these situations, counselling can help you to understand what is going on and to establish a normal relationship once the baby is out of special care.

Babies With A Disability

Learning that your new baby has a physical or mental disability brings with it a whole host of conflicting emotions. Your joy at having a new baby is tempered by confusion about what exactly the problem is, along with distress, denial, guilt, worry and disappointment. Many parents find it takes time to come to terms with the fact that their baby is not going to be 'normal'; there may be feelings of guilt or failure that you have not produced the perfect child the world expects. You may also find it hard to establish a bond with him; some parents find a physical deformity repelling (because it's not 'normal') and that stops them from interacting with the baby in a natural way, or as much as they feel they should, and this nurtures guilt.

Another hurdle is other people's reactions. After you have accepted your baby's disability, you then have to tell other people and to get used to their responses; even dealing with sympathy can be difficult.

Ann is mother to three-year-old Gilly, who has Down's syndrome:

> *'When she was first born, people always said, "Oh, I'm sorry". I thought, why are they saying that? Is Gilly substandard so they feel they have to commiserate with me? Or do they feel sorry for me? I didn't feel sorry for myself. We'd accepted the fact that Gilly had Down's and were getting on with life. But I hated telling other people about it. In the end, I stopped saying anything and just*

endured the sideway stares, but it cut me off. I became very isolated and depressed. I didn't stop loving Gilly, I just couldn't be bothered to do anything. I cared for Gilly to the exclusion of anything else and I have to say she was the one who kept me going. Finally, my partner persuaded me to see a doctor, who prescribed antidepressants and gave me the phone number of a local Down's support group. It was a slow climb, but taking the pills gave me the kick I needed to get out more and the other parents at the support group were great.'

A severely disabled baby is an enormous life-change for parents as it alters all our expectations about the future. Accepting that you have a child who will perhaps never be independent can be a daunting and depressing long-term vision which parents are in the most part unprepared for and need help and support in coming to terms with.

If you are becoming depressed, again, it is vital to seek help quickly as you are in a particularly challenging position with a very demanding baby. Doctors and other involved health professionals – as well as the specialist caregivers you are in contact with – will understand what you are going through and how important emotional support is. Support groups for your baby's disability are an invaluable source of advice and encouragement through difficult times. They can also inform you about what practical and medical help you are entitled to and how to go about getting that assistance.

You should make sure, too, that you talk to your partner honestly about your feelings and encourage him to do likewise, even if those feelings are negative. Only if you are honest can you both find ways to cope, remain close, and move forward.

Lastly, try not to compare your baby with others. Your child is unique, and therefore incomparable. Judge his progress and achievements on that basis only, and take one day at a time.

Your child can also come to monopolize your life, so that you end up with little life separate from him, a situation which is unhealthy for both of you. A happy, fulfilled mother will be a more positive person to be around, rather than someone who feels albeit, subconsciously, that she has sacrificed her life to her child. So make sure that you have outside interests and activities which allow you scope to relax and be yourself.

IF YOUR BABY DIES

Every parent thinks 'what if . . .' and prays they will never have to experience the death of their baby. It is the most unthinkable of events. We all hope to see our children grow up, build lives of their own, and outlive us. It is a sad fact, nonetheless, that some babies do die, whether it is a stillbirth, a little after the birth due to illness, or later through illness, accident or sudden infant death.

Miscarriage – too often ignored in this context – is for many women nevertheless the death of a much-wanted baby.

We know that having a previous child bereavement like cot death or miscarriage can increase the risk of postnatal depression developing with a subsequent baby but depression may also be one of the gamut of emotions parents experience directly following the death of a baby.

Grieving is very different from actual depression, although many of the outward signs are the same. Grieving is actually a necessary process which allows bereaved parents to put their child to rest in their own minds and come to terms with what has happened. It involves initially disbelief or denial, then anger, guilt, fear, great sadness, and finally acceptance and resolution, and the ability to move on. Bereaved parents feel angry because they cannot understand why their baby has been taken away, and this anger can travel in unlikely directions: at the world, because it spins on regardless; at other parents who have not lost a baby and are happy; at God and even towards the baby himself for not living, and for putting parents through this heartache. Guilt tends to focus on what you did or did not do which may have contributed towards the death, even though in the vast majority of cases, there is absolutely no issue of blame.

Fear of death and the unknown can also feature strongly, and in this parents need to find their own answers and comfort. Having strong religious beliefs can be helpful, as it may provide you with comfort and an acceptance of why a child has died. It can also remove the fear of death if you believe your child is in a heaven, or moving to another life, with loved ones who have gone before or simply beyond suffering.

Coming through this period of grieving without having reached an acceptance of the death can cause depression to develop, but this is not postnatal depression. If you are in this situation, consult your doctor or a support organization or a bereavement counsellor (see Useful Addresses for more information). There are also many excellent books which have been written specifically on bereavement and offer much more in-depth advice and support.

CHAPTER 8

Life After Postnatal Depression

From the depths of depression it is often hard to envisage a time when you will not feel this way. But, once you seek help for the illness, many women are surprised at how quickly their recovery starts. At this stage, you will begin to see light at the end of the tunnel, and you will hopefully want to do more to push the depression out of the way once and for all. The self-help sections of this book will come into their own at this time and you can set about getting your family life together in other ways too.

GET CLOSE TO YOUR BABY

If the depression has left you feeling that you have not properly got close to your baby, make an effort to establish close contact now. If the depression made it difficult for you to hold and hug your baby, do things which encourage closeness now but which will not suddenly overwhelm her with demands for affection. Dancing, bedtime cuddles, reading books together, will all introduce closeness. Baby massage is also a lovely way to help mother and baby to get more in touch with each other.

Later, introduce finger and action rhymes. There are many good children's nursery rhyme books around, if you do not remember them from your own childhood. These get you doing things together and having fun; other games which require your help include simple jigsaws, shape sorters and, of course, first books. When you do play with baby, get down to her level – sit or lie down on the floor – and try not to monopolize the play activity. Give baby space to play with her toys without interfering or taking over.

DO THINGS TOGETHER AS A FAMILY

Try to get out with the baby at least once a day. This gives you both fresh air, a change of scenery, and an injection of interest. Find out what children's clubs and activity centres are open in your area and sign up for a few. Many sports centres run children's activities and baby movement classes at reasonable prices. You may also find baby music and dance classes, story-telling and toddler clubs where they can play with other toys, meet other children of the same age and where you can meet other mothers. In the summer there are parks (which often have entertainment for children), open farms and animal parks. In winter, look out for indoor soft-play centres, which usually contain areas for babies as well as a multitude of toys and climbing apparatus.

But it does not have to be as organized as this. Trips to the playpark, to feed the ducks, to the shops, around the mall, feeding squirrels . . . Children find variety wherever they go and their enthusiasms will surprise you. My youngest son, at one-and-a-half years old, got most pleasure from 'stick walks', which meant going anywhere he could pick up twigs, take home a carefully selected collection and sort these at his leisure. In truth, young children are usually content to be with their parent, doing something together. It is the togetherness which matters more than the activity itself.

CONTINUE TO MAKE TIME FOR YOURSELF

Taking time out for yourself is as important once you have your depression under control as it was in fighting it: you need space and time to be that other person in you who is not all-providing. Read back over the suggestions for 'Me Time' (see p. 79) and put them into practice if you are finding that family demands are making in-roads into your space now that your depression is gone.

COMMUNICATION WITH YOUR PARTNER

Talking with your partner remains vital even after the depression is behind you. The needs of a young child can make you neglect your own needs as a couple and keeping communication channels open – so that you can discuss your feelings (both negative and positive) – will keep you close.

As your baby grows up, talk to each other about child-care issues: how you are going to approach problems, keep a united front on discipline, and so on. It is all part of developing a supportive bedrock for your child to rely on.

It is also important that you and your partner have time together on your own, to keep your relationship fresh and to strike a balance between being yourselves as adults and yourselves as parents. Try to arrange a babysitter once a week so that you can go out; keep to this even if you are tired, as the effort can recharge your batteries as much as a few hours' extra sleep. You do not have to do anything demanding: a drink out or to see a film is enough. The vital element is the togetherness and the time it gives you to talk and re-establish contact with each other in a non-domestic environment.

ENJOY LIFE

Enjoying life is not a case of doing what you want; it is making the most of what comes along and not feeling frightened to be happy. Simply enjoy moments with your baby that are calm, precious and rewarding without allowing any negative thoughts or worries to impinge. We sometimes worry so much about the future, about our own situation and feelings, that we don't see the pleasures that are under our noses. So try to stop worrying, think positively and squeeze as much out of your life, because that way you are recreating yourself as a positive, happier person.

ENJOY YOUR BABY

If you are depressed, it is easy to overlook the positive side of being a parent but there are many wonderful moments that give you back a good return for all your hard work, if only you stop and have time to enjoy life with a baby.

There are many small milestones along with the big developments: learning to sit up, crawl and take a spoonful of food; her persistent attempts to pull herself up or roll over once she gets curious about the world; the first smile and giggle at something you do; her quick ability to work out the activity centre and then rattle the life out of it; her first slow scan of a room and the way her face lights up when her gaze settles on you; the first time she shows a food preference and you realize she does not like carrots, but cannot get enough pear purée; her joy at discovering the world contains animals – and those first little animal imitations; the way she takes to action rhymes and tickling games, so soon she is asking you to play; the look of surprise when she first takes a toddling step, and a tumble; her excitement at going on the swings or down the slide at the playpark; ducks in the park; ice-cream (the first taste and the messy face); watching her play with other children, then wanting to join in, and later, learning how to share; the cuddles; the kissing-better; and the angelic face when she is sleeping.

The list is endless. These are only the things I remember about my own babies, but you will have many more of your own which can light up your heart when you think about them. These warming moments change as your baby grows up, but they provide you with a constant kaleidoscope of positive experiences which see you through the times when, yes, they are little devils.

The trick to establishing a happy family life is, as in all things, balance. Once you have established a balanced approach to childcare, in your relationships with those around you, and of course within yourself, it is easier to deal with problems as they arise, from a position of confidence.

YOUR NEXT BABY

When you start thinking about having another baby, it is natural to worry that you will develop postnatal depression again.

The first thing to say here is that it is by no means a foregone conclusion that you will develop postnatal depression second-time around. Much depends on how severe your depression was the first time and what your circumstances are as you go in for baby number two. You may no longer have the pressures on you that were significant in triggering postnatal depression last time. The birth this time may go more smoothly, the second baby may not be such a constant crier, your partner – knowing what your needs are – may help out more. But probably the greatest defence against developing postnatal depression again is the fact that you are now comfortable with being a mother and your partner has grown into the role of father. Second-timers are usually more relaxed about things like babycare problems, keeping up appearances and doing everything 'just so', which means they cut down significantly on the stress they went through with their first baby.

Unfortunately, however, some mothers do go on to develop postnatal depression again with subsequent babies, particularly if they had severe postnatal depression or suffer from depression generally. But at least the next time around you will be more prepared and will recognize the signs of postnatal depression developing. This will allow you to seek help quickly. The health professionals you come into contact with – both during pregnancy and after the birth – will be keeping a close eye on your progress, too.

You can help yourself, too, assessing whether there is anything which contributed to your last postnatal depression which is still a problem this time around. You can then take steps to tackle it before it has a chance to exert an effect. This may mean ensuring you have a good network of supporters around you, that your partner takes sufficient time off work, when the baby is born or that you have time to yourself every day. It will also help to re-read the self-help sections of this book to prepare yourself for baby-care difficulties, refresh your memory on dealing with stress, and to get yourself into a positive frame of mind.

Postnatal depression is an illness which can be beaten and from which you and your family emerge intact.

'I can't believe what I was like then, when I think back,' admits Felicity. *'The black despair. The numbness. The guilt that I couldn't love my baby like the other mothers loved theirs. But now, I don't know what I'd do without her. I look back at photos of Libby as a newborn and I know that I loved her then, too. The depression just covered it up for a while. She's a gorgeous little girl and she's helped me not to feel such a failure. I'm her mother and that seems to be enough for her.'*

You, too, will be able to look back on your postnatal depression at some point and know that you loved your baby, even through the blackness – and that is all any child wants from its parents.

Further Reading

BEREAVEMENT

Markham, U, *Bereavement: Your Questions Answered*, Element, 1996
A supportive, informative read if you have lost a baby.

BREASTFEEDING

Renfrew, M, Fisher, C and Arms, S, *Getting Breastfeeding Right for You*, Celestial Arts, 1990
Excellent, supportive book to get you on the right track with breastfeeding.

COMPLEMENTARY THERAPY

Curtis, S, *Essential Oils*, Aurum, 1996
Schmidt, S, *Inner Harmony Through Bach Flowers*, Time-Life, 1997
Guide to using Bach flower remedies
Worwood, V A, *The Fragrant Pharmacy*, Bantam, 1995
Useful guides for using aromatherapy at home.

DEPRESSION

Breton, S, *Depression: Your Questions Answered*, Element, 1996
An informative introduction to general depression and its psychotherapeutic treatments.
Dalton, K with Holton, W, *Depression After Childbirth*, Oxford University Press, 1996
Gilbert, P, *Overcoming Depression*, Robinson, 1997

Explains Dr Dalton's preventive progesterone programme for postnatal depression.

Stewart, M and Stewart, Dr A, *Everywoman's Health Guide*, Headline, 1997

Clear guidelines on a nutritional approach to helping women's health problems, including depression.

INFERTILITY

Bryan, E and Higgins, R, *Infertility: New Choices, New Dilemmas*, Penguin, 1995

For anyone who has undergone, or is undergoing, fertility treatment.

References

1. *The Lancet*, April 6 1996, v347, n9006
2. *British Medical Journal*, April 9 1994, v 308, n6934
3. Parenting in the 1990s: report from the Social Statistics Research Unit, City University, London, published 1996
4. *British Medical Journal*, 1996 v313: 253–8
5. *The Lancet*, February 1996, v347

Useful Addresses

Australia

Australian Natural Therapists
   Association
7 Highview Grove
Burwood East
Victoria 3151
*Contact for referral to individual
therapies.*

Bereaved Parents Support
   Centre
Lower Parish Hall
300 Camberwell Rd
Camberwell 3124

Mental Health Foundation
Mental Health Education and
   Resource Centre
Tweedie Place
Richmond
Victoria 3121

Nursing Mothers Association
5 Glendale St
Nunawading 3131

Post and Antenatal Depression
   Association
1st Floor
Canterbury Family Centre
19 Canterbury Rd
Camberwell
Victoria 3124

Canada

Canadian Holistic Medical
   Association
42 Redpath Avenue

Toronto
Ontario M4S 2J6

Canadian Mental Health Association
2160 Yonge St
3rd Floor
Toronto
Ontario M4S 2Z3

International Baby Food Action
   Network (IBFAN)
10 Trinity Square
Toronto
Ontario
*For breastfeeding counsellors in your
area.*

United Kingdom

Association for Postnatal Illness
25 Jerdan Place
London SW6 1BE

British Association for Counselling
1 Regent Place
Rugby
Warks CV21 2PJ

British Register of Complementary
   Practitioners
PO Box 194
London SE16 1QZ
*For referral to individual complementary
therapy organizations.*

CHILD
PO Box 154
Hounslow
Middx TW5 0EZ
For fertility treatment-linked problems.

Compassionate Friends
53 North St
Bristol BS3 1EN

Cry-sis Support Group
BM Cry-sis
London WC1N 3XX
For problems with a crying baby

Foundation for the Study of Infant
  Deaths
35 Belgrave Square
London SW1X 8QB

Gingerbread
35 Wellington St
London WC2E 7BN
For single parents

La Leche League
BM3424
London WC1N 3XX

MAMA (Meet a Mum Association)
14 Willis Rd
Croydon CR0 2XX

MIND
Granta House
15–19 Broadway
Stratford, London E15 4BQ

National Childbirth Trust
Alexandra House
Oldham Terrace
Acton
London W3 6NH
*For breastfeeding problems and postnatal
support groups*

RELATE (National Marriage Council)
Herbert Gray College

Little Church St
Rugby
Warks CV21 3AP

Stillbirth and Neonatal Death Society
  (SANDS)
28 Portland Place
London W1N 4DE

Twins and Multiple Births
  Association (TAMBA)
PO Box 30
Little Sutton
South Wirral
L66 1TH

United States

American Mental Health Foundation
2 East 86th St
New York, NY 1008

Compassionate Friends
PO Box 3696
Oak Brook
Illinois 60522–3696

Depression After Delivery (DAD)
PO Box 59973
Renton
WA 98058

La Leche League International
PO Box 1209
Franklin Park
IL 60131–8209

Postpartum Support International
927 North Kellogg Avenue
Santa Barbara
California 93111

Index